PRIMARY MATHEMATICS

EXTRA PRACTICE 2

Common Core Edition

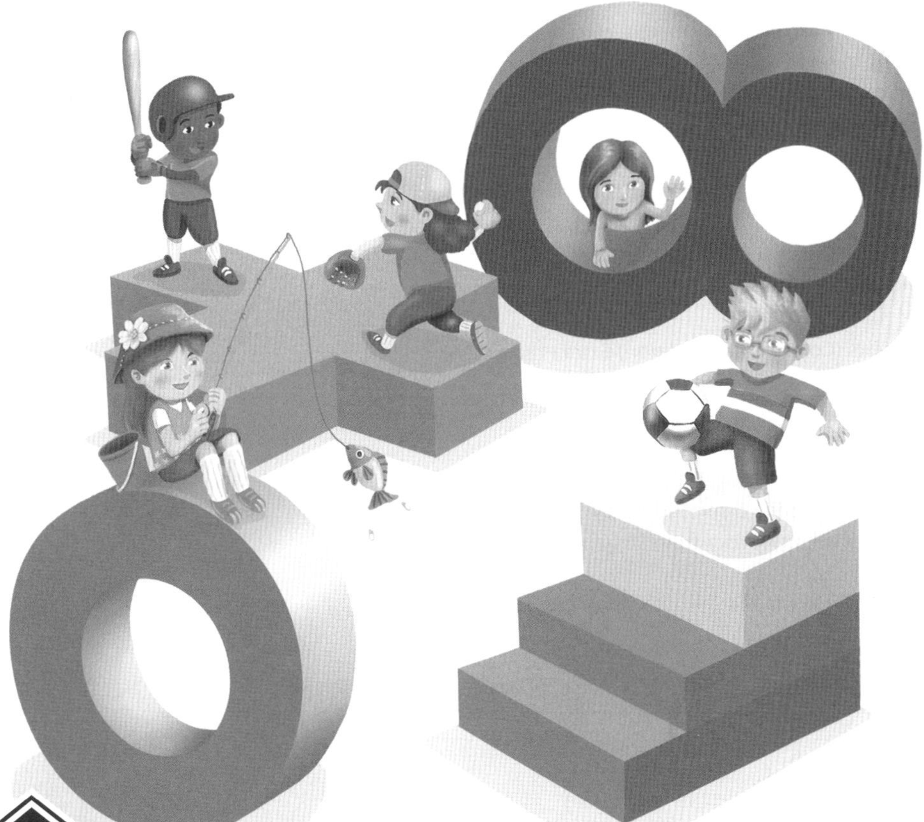

SINGAPORE MATH® PROGRAM

Lim Kian Chu

Marshall Cavendish Education

AF080363

© 2008 Marshall Cavendish International (Singapore) Private Limited

This edition © 2014 Marshall Cavendish Education Pte Ltd

Published by Marshall Cavendish Education
Times Centre, 1 New Industrial Road, Singapore 536196
Customer Service Hotline: (65) 6213 9688
US Office Tel: (+1-914) 332 8888 | Fax: (+1-914) 332 8882
E-mail: cs@mceducation.com
Website: www.mceducation.com

First published 2008
New edition 2014
Reprinted 2014, 2015, 2018, 2019 (twice), 2020, 2021

All rights reserved.

No part of this publication may be reproduced, stored in a retrieval system
or transmitted, in any form or by any means, electronic, mechanical,
photocopying, recording or otherwise, without the prior permission
of the copyright owner. Any requests for permission should be
addressed to the Publisher.

Marshall Cavendish is a registered trademark of Times Publishing Limited.

Singapore Math® is a trademark of Singapore Math Inc.® and
Marshall Cavendish Education Pte Ltd.

Primary Mathematics (Common Core Edition) Extra Practice 2
ISBN 978-981-01-9864-0

Printed in Singapore

We would like to acknowledge contributions by:
Jennifer Kempe (Curriculum Advisor from Singapore Math Inc.®)

Preface

PRIMARY MATHEMATICS Common Core Edition Extra Practice is a series of five supplementary books.

This series follows the topical arrangement in the Primary Mathematics (Common Core Edition) Textbooks and Workbooks. Friendly Notes at the beginning of each unit provide a source for reference and revision of concepts. The level of difficulty, as well as the style of the problems, is similar to the exercises in the Textbooks and Workbooks. The short and topic-specific exercises enable instructors to assign work only in those topics in which the student needs more practice. This, together with the simple language used, allows students to review mathematics with minimal guidance.

Primary Mathematics (Common Core Edition) Extra Practice aims to consolidate and reinforce the mathematical skills taught in the Primary Mathematics series. Students will master mathematical concepts with confidence through the use of this series.

Contents

Unit 1	**Numbers to 1,000**	1
Exercise 1	Looking Back	5
Exercise 2	Counting Within 1,000	9
Exercise 3	Comparing Numbers	13
Unit 2	**Addition and Subtraction**	15
Exercise 1A	Looking Back	23
Exercise 1B	Looking Back	25
Exercise 2	Addition Without Renaming	27
Exercise 3	Subtraction Without Renaming	29
Exercise 4A	Addition With Renaming	33
Exercise 4B	Addition With Renaming	35
Exercise 5A	Subtraction With Renaming	37
Exercise 5B	Subtraction With Renaming	39
Unit 3	**Length**	41
Exercise 1	Measuring Length	45
Exercise 2	Measuring Length in Meters	47
Exercise 3	Measuring Length in Centimeters	49
Exercise 4	Other Units of Length	51
Unit 4	**Multiplication and Division**	55
Exercise 1	Multiplication	57
Exercise 2	Division	63
Unit 5	**Multiplication Tables of 2 and 3**	69
Exercise 1	Multiplication Table of 2	73
Exercise 2	Multiplication Table of 3	77
Exercise 3	Dividing by 2	83
Exercise 4	Dividing by 3	87
Exercise 5	Remainders	91
Unit 6	**Addition and Subtraction**	93
Exercise 1	Finding the Missing Number	97
Exercise 2	Methods for Mental Addition	99
Exercise 3	Methods for Mental Subtraction	101

Unit 7	**Multiplication and Division**	105
Exercise 1	Multiplying and Dividing by 4	109
Exercise 2	Multiplying and Dividing by 5	113
Exercise 3	Multiplying and Dividing by 10	115
Unit 8	**Money**	117
Exercise 1	Dollars and Cents	121
Exercise 2	Adding Money	125
Exercise 3	Subtracting Money	129
Unit 9	**Fractions**	131
Exercise 1	Halves, Fourths, and Thirds	135
Exercise 2	Writing Fractions	137
Unit 10	**Time**	143
Exercise 1	Telling Time After the Hour	145
Exercise 2	Telling Time Before the Hour	147
Unit 11	**Tables and Graphs**	149
Exercise 1	Picture Graphs	153
Exercise 2	Bar Graphs	157
Exercise 3	Line Plots	159
Unit 12	**Geometry**	161
Exercise 1	Flat and Curved Surfaces	167
Exercise 2	Composite Figures	169
Exercise 3	Angles and Shapes	171
Answers		173

BLANK

Unit 1 : Numbers to 1,000

Friendly Notes

Counting Within 1,000

We can group big numbers into hundreds, tens, and ones. This makes counting easy.

1. Count the straws.

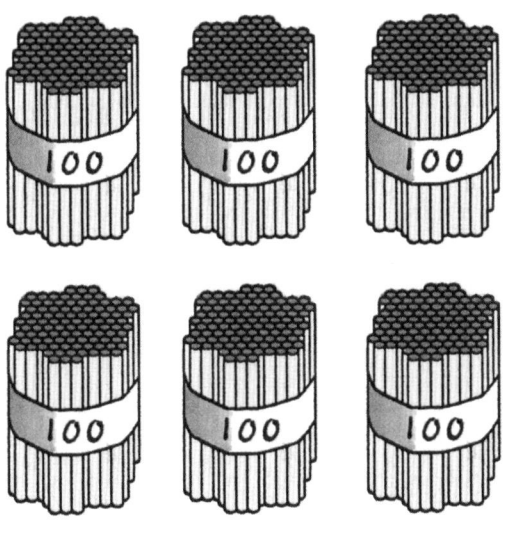

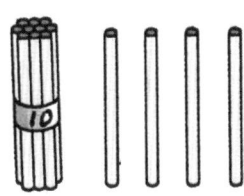

100, 200, 300, 400, 500, 600, 610, 611, 612, 613, 614

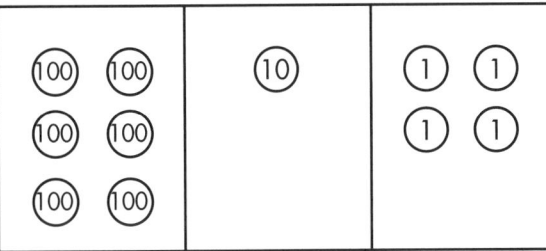

6 hundreds 1 ten 4 ones = 614
600 + 10 + 4 = 614

We put 10 tens together to make a hundred.
We put 10 hundreds together to make a thousand.

2. This is a one-hundred-dollar bill.

We can exchange 10 ten-dollar bills for a one-hundred-dollar bill.

Comparing Numbers

When we compare numbers, we work from left to right.

1. Which number is greater?

H	T	O
1	8	9
3	0	2

189   302

First, compare the hundreds.

3 hundreds is greater than 1 hundred.

302 is greater than 189.
302 > 189

'>' means greater than.

2. Which number is smaller?

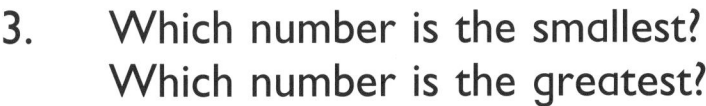

H	T	O
2	**8**	5
2	**5**	5

First, compare the hundreds.
They are the same.

Next, compare the tens.
5 tens is smaller than 8 tens.
So, 255 is smaller than 285.
255 < 285

'<' means less than.

3. Which number is the smallest?
Which number is the greatest?

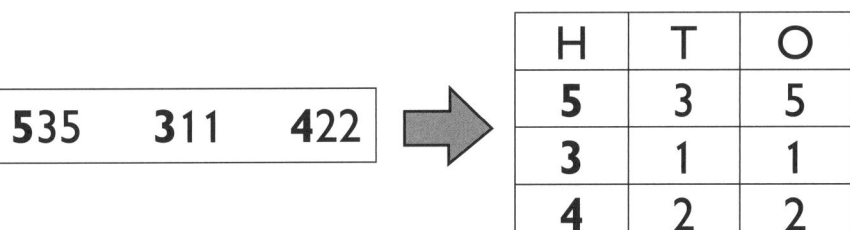

H	T	O
5	3	5
3	1	1
4	2	2

First, compare the hundreds.
3 hundreds is less than 5 hundreds and 4 hundreds.
So, 311 is the smallest number.

5 hundreds is greater than 4 hundreds and 3 hundreds.
So, 535 is the greatest number.

To make the smallest or greatest possible number from a group of numbers, place the numbers in a chart. Then compare the numbers from left to right.

4. What is the smallest number that can be made using 6, 2, and 8?

H	T	O	
6	2	8	✗
6	8	2	✗
8	6	2	✗
8	2	6	✗
2	6	8	
2	8	6	✗

Compare the hundreds.
2 hundreds is smaller than 6 hundreds and 8 hundreds.
So, we look at 286 and 268 only.

Compare the tens.
6 tens is smaller than 8 tens.
So, **268** is the smallest number.

268 = 200 + 60 + 8
286 = 200 + 80 + 6
80 is greater than 60.
286 is greater than 268.

Exercise 1 : Looking Back

1. Match.

Seventy-eight

Forty-five

Ninety

Nineteen

Fifty-three

Thirty-four

2. Write the numbers.

   (a) thirty-six = ☐

   (b) sixty = ☐

   (c) seventy-two = ☐

   (d) eighteen = ☐

   (e) one hundred = ☐

   (f) twenty-three = ☐

   (g) fifty = ☐

3. Fill in the boxes.

   (a) 10 less than 35 is ☐.

   (b) 2 less than 67 is ☐.

   (c) 1 more than 79 is ☐.

   (d) 2 more than 38 is ☐.

   (e) ☐ is 10 more than 90.

   (f) ☐ is 5 less than 70.

   (g) 6 less than 12 is ☐.

   (h) ☐ is 8 less than 23.

   (i) ☐ is 6 more than 31.

   (j) 3 more than 33 is ☐.

4. Fill in the boxes.

(a) 59 − 10 = ☐   (b) 60 − 1 = ☐
(c) 30 − 20 = ☐   (d) 100 − 99 = ☐
(e) 80 − 76 = ☐   (f) 27 − 20 = ☐
(g) 30 + 8 = ☐   (h) 58 + 2 = ☐
(i) 58 + 20 = ☐   (j) 65 − 10 = ☐
(k) 76 − 72 = ☐   (l) 83 + 10 = ☐
(m) 27 − 26 = ☐   (n) 92 − 12 = ☐
(o) 45 + 30 = ☐   (p) 50 + 9 = ☐
(q) 62 + 10 = ☐   (r) 78 + 2 = ☐

5. Write the numbers in words.

(a) 15 _____
(b) 27 _____
(c) 46 _____
(d) 55 _____
(e) 94 _____
(f) 77 _____
(g) 38 _____

6. Fill in the boxes.

    (a) What number is 1 more than 29? ☐

    (b) What number is 2 more than 93? ☐

    (c) What number is 1 less than 66? ☐

    (d) What number is 10 less than 76? ☐

    (e) What number is 2 more than 57? ☐

    (f) What number is 20 more than 66? ☐

    (g) What number is 20 more than 43? ☐

    (h) What number is 2 less than 74? ☐

    (i) What number is 5 more than 82? ☐

    (j) What number is 5 more than 26? ☐

7. Fill in the boxes.

    (a) 1 ten 8 ones = ☐

    (b) 2 tens 3 ones = ☐

    (c) ☐ tens 6 ones = 46

    (d) ☐ tens 7 ones = 57

    (e) 6 tens ☐ ones = 69

    (f) 8 tens ☐ ones = 80

Exercise 2 : Counting Within 1,000

1. Match.

Five hundred seventeen •	•  812
Six hundred twenty-nine •	•  408
Eight hundred twelve •	•  570
Four hundred eight •	• 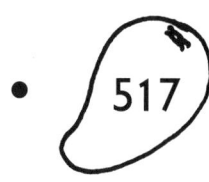 517
Five hundred seventy •	•  629

2. Fill in the boxes.

   (a) 4 hundreds 5 tens 8 ones = ▢

   (b) 2 hundreds 7 ones = ▢

   (c) ▢ hundreds 9 ones = 909

   (d) 7 hundreds 8 tens = ▢

   (e) 6 hundreds ▢ tens = 640

   (f) 5 hundreds 9 tens ▢ ones = 597

3. What number does each chart show?

   (a), (b), (c), (d)

4. Fill in the boxes and blanks.

   (a) What number is 1 less than 900? ▢

   (b) What number is 1 more than 502? ▢

   (c) What number is 10 less than 613? ▢

   (d) What number is 10 less than 192? ▢

   (e) What number is 100 less than 568? ▢

   (f) What number is 100 more than 765? ▢

   (g) We can exchange _____ ten-dollar bills for a one-hundred-dollar bill.

   (h) We can exchange _____ one-hundred-dollar bills for a one-thousand-dollar bill.

5. Write the numbers in words.

   (a) 213 _____

   (b) 350 _____

   (c) 515 _____

   (d) 640 _____

   (e) 809 _____

   (f) 442 _____

   (g) 198 _____

   (h) 375 _____

   (i) 777 _____

   (j) 989 _____

6. Fill in the boxes.

   (a) 900 + 100 = ☐

   (b) 286 + 100 = ☐

   (c) 798 + 100 = ☐

   (d) 382 + 10 = ☐

   (e) 800 − 100 = ☐

   (f) 970 − 10 = ☐

   (g) 170 − 100 = ☐

   (h) 210 − 100 = ☐

7. Write the missing numbers.

   (a) 100 + 30 + 6 = ☐

   (b) 800 + 5 = ☐

   (c) 700 + 70 = ☐

   (d) 5 + 40 + 300 = ☐

   (e) ☐ + 80 + 7 = 487

   (f) 600 + 60 + ☐ = 661

   (g) 500 + ☐ + 9 = 529

   (h) ☐ + 8 = 908

Primary Mathematics (Common Core Edition) Extra Practice 2

Name: _____ Class: _____ Date: _____

Exercise 3 : Comparing Numbers

1. Circle the greater number.

   (a) | 45 | 54 | (b) | 170 | 168 | (c) | 198 | 189 |

2. Circle the smaller number.

   (a) | 66 | 69 | (b) | 445 | 485 | (c) | 290 | 281 |

3. Write > or < in each ◯.

   (a) 122 ◯ 235   (b) 254 ◯ 246

4. Circle the greatest number.

   (a) | 36 | 34 | 35 | (b) | 159 | 260 | 262 |

   (c) | 165 | 366 | 163 | (d) | 479 | 384 | 482 |

   (e) | 280 | 175 | 279 | 382 | (f) | 191 | 389 | 390 | 188 |

   (g) | 421 | 312 | 423 | 132 | (h) | 546 | 164 | 284 | 548 |

5. Circle the smallest number.

   (a) | 225 | 231 | 228 |

   (b) | 156 | 165 | 170 |

   (c) | 176 | 169 | 258 |

   (d) | 369 | 296 | 156 |

   (e) | 190 | 288 | 193 | 292 |

   (f) | 599 | 189 | 198 | 590 |

   (g) | 228 | 382 | 318 | 381 |

   (h) | 651 | 569 | 684 | 696 |

6. Arrange the numbers in order.

   (a) Begin with the smallest.

   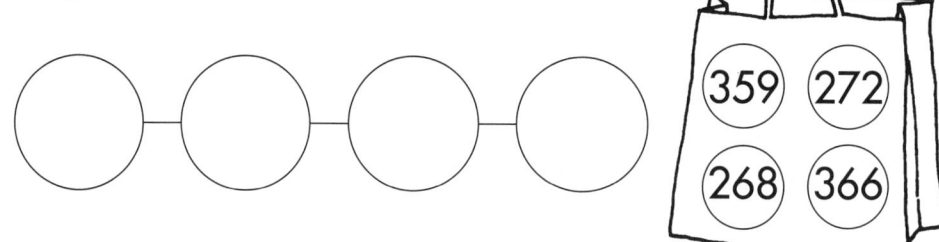

   (b) Begin with the greatest.

   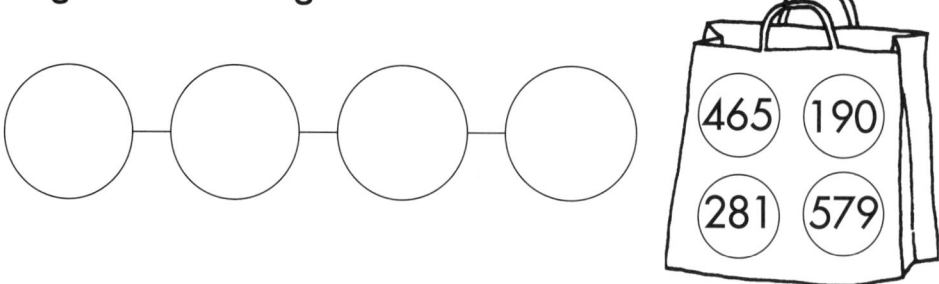

7. Complete the regular number pattern.

   123, 133, _____, _____, 163, 173, _____

Unit 2 : Addition and Subtraction

Friendly Notes

Meanings of Addition and Subtraction

We add two parts to find the whole.
We subtract one part from the whole to find the other part.

1. Paul has 6 balls.
   Amanda has 4 balls.
   How many balls are there altogether?

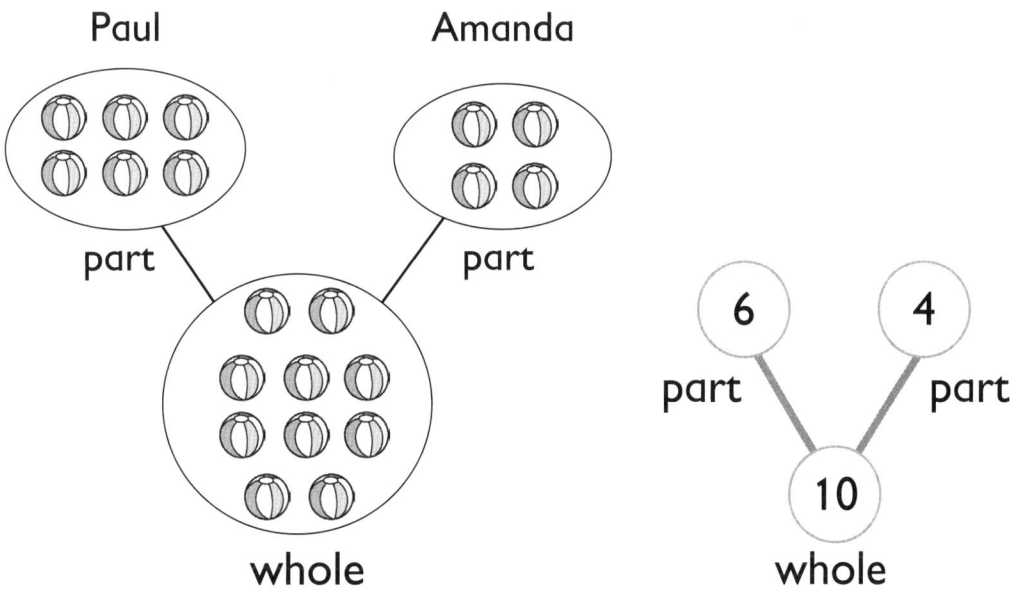

   6 + 4 = 10
   There are 10 balls altogether.

2. 　 8 + 5 = 13　　5 + 8 = 13
　　　13 − 5 = 8　　13 − 8 = 5

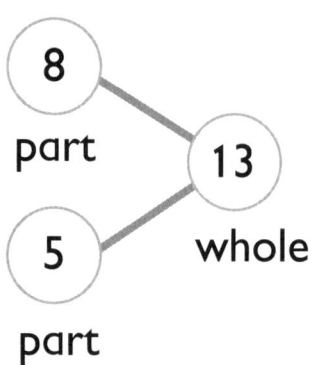

3. Maria has 45 books in her room.
   June has 24 books.
   How many books do they have altogether?

   45 + 24 = 69

   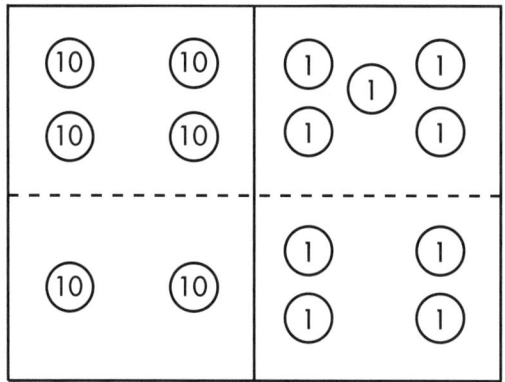

   They have 69 books altogether.

4. Carlos and Eric bought 36 stickers.
   Carlos bought 22 stickers.
   How many stickers did Eric buy?

   36 − 22 = 14

   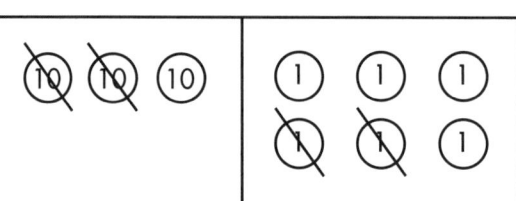

   Eric bought 14 stickers.

Addition Without Renaming

When we add two numbers, we can write one number on top of the other.
Make sure the digits are arranged in the correct columns.

432 + 54 = _____

```
  H T O
  4 3 2
+   5 4
  -----
```
This is wrong!

In the number 54, the digit 5 stands for 5 tens.
The digit 4 stands for 4 ones.

```
  H T O
  4 3 2
+     5 4
  -------
```
This is correct!

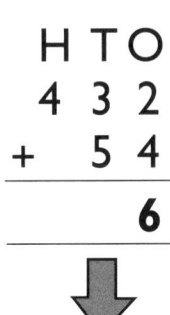

Add the ones.

```
  H T O
  4 3 2
+     5 4
  -------
        6
```

Add the tens.

```
  H T O
  4 3 2
+     5 4
  -------
      8 6
```

Add the hundreds.

```
  H T O
  4 3 2
+     5 4
  -------
  4 8 6
```

432 + 54 = 486

Subtraction Without Renaming

When we subtract one number from another, we always write the greater number on top. Make sure the digits are arranged in the correct columns.

368 − 65 = _____

```
  H T O
  3 6 8
−   6 5
─────────
```
This is wrong!

In the number 65, the digit 6 stands for 6 tens. The digit 5 stands for 5 ones.

```
  H T O
  3 6 8
−     6 5
─────────
```
This is correct!

Subtract the ones.
```
  H T O
  3 6 8
−     6 5
─────────
        3
```

Subtract the tens.
```
  H T O
  3 6 8
−     6 5
─────────
      0 3
```

Subtract the hundreds.

368 − 65 = 303
```
  H T O
  3 6 8
−     6 5
─────────
  3 0 3
```

Addition With Renaming

When there are 10 ones or more, change 10 ones for 1 ten. When there are 10 tens or more, change 10 tens for 1 hundred.

Add 156 and 176.

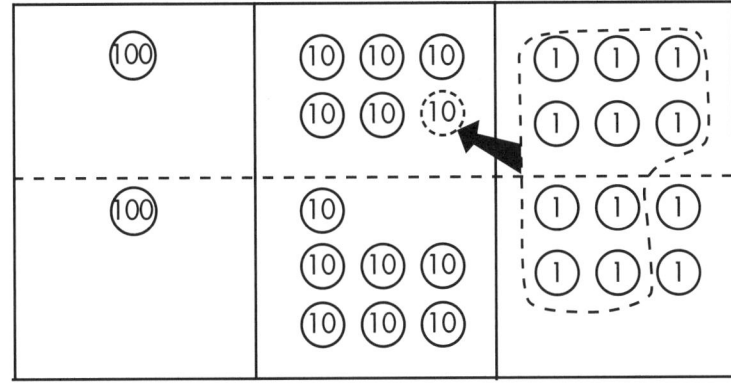

Add the ones.
6 ones + 6 ones
= 12 ones
= 1 ten 2 ones

$$\begin{array}{r} \overset{1}{1\ 5\ 6} \\ +1\ 7\ 6 \\ \hline 2 \end{array}$$

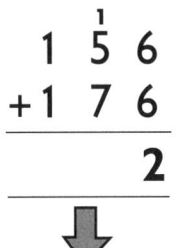

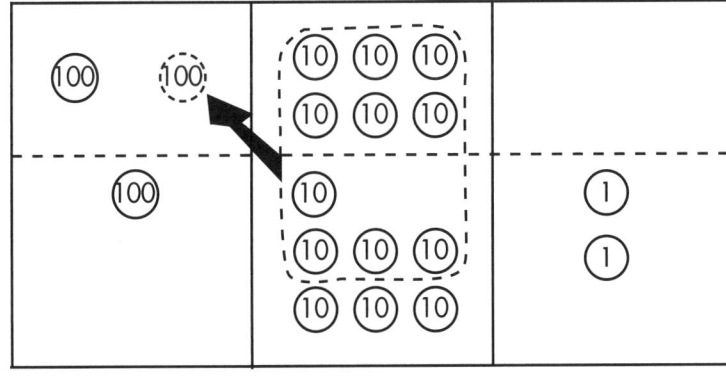

Add the tens.
5 tens + 7 tens + 1 ten
= 13 tens
= 1 hundred 3 tens

$$\begin{array}{r} \overset{1}{1}\ \overset{1}{5}\ 6 \\ +1\ 7\ 6 \\ \hline 3\ 2 \end{array}$$

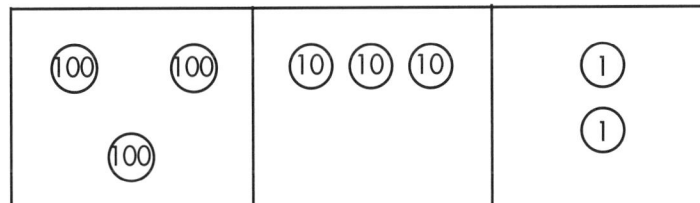

Add the hundreds.

$$\begin{array}{r} \overset{1}{1}\ \overset{1}{5}\ 6 \\ +1\ 7\ 6 \\ \hline 3\ 3\ 2 \end{array}$$

156 + 176 = 332

Subtraction With Renaming

When there are not enough ones to take away from, change 1 ten for 10 ones.

1. Subtract 543 from 731.

We cannot take away 3 ones from 1 one.

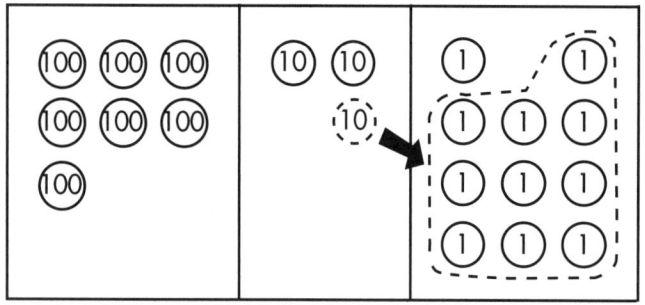

Change 1 ten for 10 ones.

$$\begin{array}{r} 7\,\overset{2}{\cancel{3}}\,\overset{11}{\cancel{1}} \\ -\,5\,4\,3 \\ \hline \end{array}$$

Subtract the ones.

$$\begin{array}{r} 7\,\overset{2}{\cancel{3}}\,\overset{11}{\cancel{1}} \\ -\,5\,4\,3 \\ \hline 8 \end{array}$$

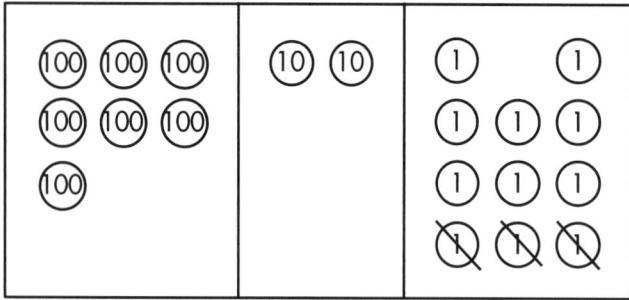

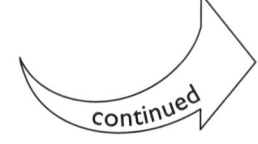

When there are not enough tens to take away from, change 1 hundred to 10 tens.

We cannot take away 4 tens from 2 tens.

Change 1 hundred for 10 tens.

Subtract the tens.

$$\begin{array}{r} {}^6\cancel{7}\,{}^{12}\cancel{3}\,{}^{11}\cancel{1} \\ -\;5\;4\;3 \\ \hline 8\;8 \end{array}$$

Subtract the hundreds.

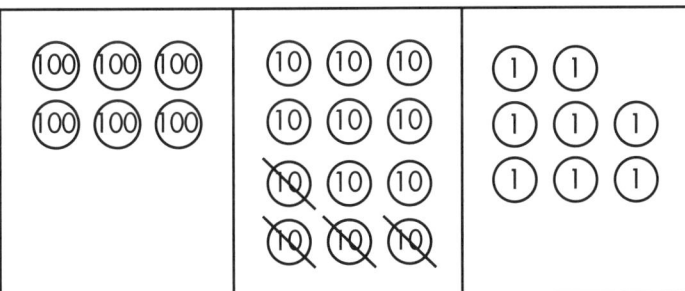

$$\begin{array}{r} {}^6\cancel{7}\,{}^{12}\cancel{3}\,{}^{11}\cancel{1} \\ -\;5\;4\;3 \\ \hline 1\;8\;8 \end{array}$$

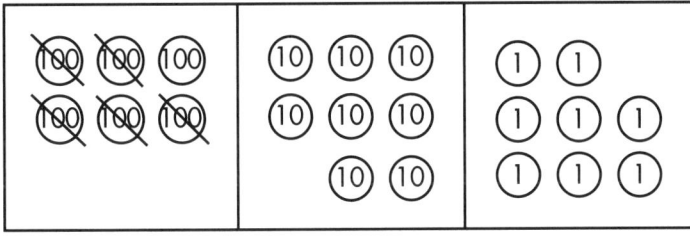

731 − 543 = 188

When there are 0 tens and ones, change 1 hundred for 9 tens and 10 ones.

2. Subtract 186 from 500.

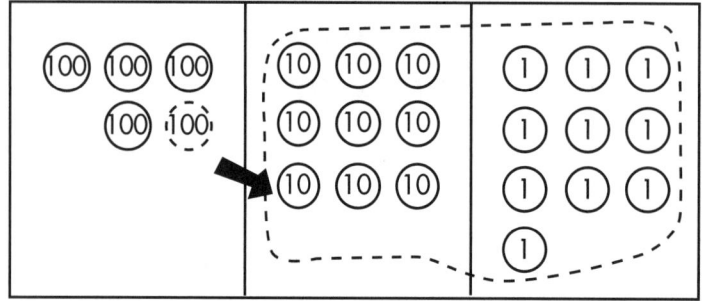

Subtract the ones.

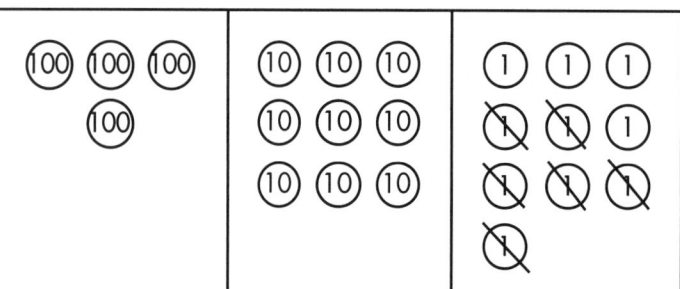

Subtract the tens.

Subtract the hundreds.

500 − 186 = 314

Exercise 1A : Looking Back

1. Add or subtract.

    (a) 8 + 14 = ☐   (b) 7 + 8 = ☐

    (c) 12 − 8 = ☐   (d) 15 − 7 = ☐

    (e) 16 + 4 = ☐   (f) 46 + 3 = ☐

    (g) 28 − 6 = ☐   (h) 55 − 9 = ☐

2. Write the missing numbers.

    (a) 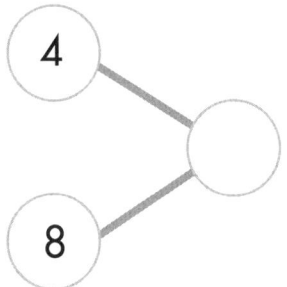   (b)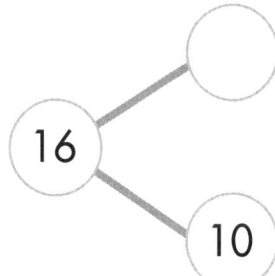

    (c) 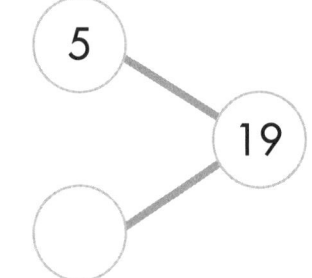   (d)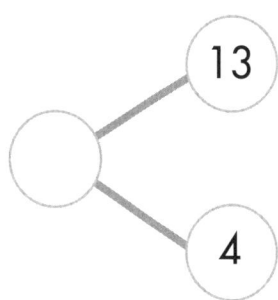

3. Fill in the boxes.

    (a) Add 20 and 68.   (b) Subtract 53 from 88.

    20 + 68 = ☐   88 − 53 = ☐

4. Write two addition equations and two subtraction equations.

Example:

26 + 38 = 64	38 + 26 = 64
64 − 26 = 38	64 − 38 = 26

(a)

(b)

(c)

Exercise 1B : Looking Back

1. Solve.

   Use a place-value chart to help you.

   (a) Tina is 25 years old.

   Her friend is 13 years older than her.

   How old is her friend?

   25 + 13 = ?

   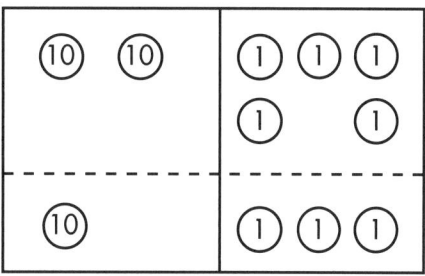

   Tina's friend is _____ years old.

   (b) After giving 57 stamps to her brother,

   Yani had 23 stamps left.

   How many stamps did she have at first?

   ☐ ○ ☐ = ☐

   Yani had _____ stamps at first.

(c) There are 32 boys and 45 girls on a field.
How many more girls than boys are there?

There are _____ more girls than boys.

(d) Maria and Jen have 39 baseball cards.
Maria has 16 baseball cards.
How many baseball cards does Jen have?

Jen has _____ baseball cards.

(e) Pet shop A has 48 hamsters.
It has 2 fewer terrapins than hamsters.
How many terrapins are there?

There are _____ terrapins.

Exercise 2 : Addition Without Renaming

1. Add.

   (a) $3 + 5 = \boxed{}$ (b) $6 + 3 = \boxed{}$

   $30 + 50 = \boxed{}$ $60 + 30 = \boxed{}$

   $300 + 500 = \boxed{}$ $600 + 300 = \boxed{}$

   (c) 653 (d) 328 (e) 405
   $+6$ $+60$ $+50$
   $\overline{}$ $\overline{}$ $\overline{}$

   (f) 530 (g) 24 (h) 36
   $+67$ $+643$ $+503$
   $\overline{}$ $\overline{}$ $\overline{}$

   (i) 428 (j) 382 (k) 724
   $+250$ $+416$ $+235$
   $\overline{}$ $\overline{}$ $\overline{}$

2. Solve.

   (a) Mike bought 67 green apples and
       532 red apples.
       How many apples did he buy in all?

       Mike bought _____ apples in all.

   (b) There were 423 boys in a school.
       There were 315 more girls than boys
       in the school.
       How many girls were there in the school?

       There were _____ girls in the school.

   (c) Mr. Ramsey baked 230 muffins on Monday.
       He baked 455 fewer muffins on Monday than
       on Tuesday.
       How many muffins did he bake on Tuesday?

       Mr. Ramsey baked _____ muffins on Tuesday.

Exercise 3 : Subtraction Without Renaming

1. Subtract.

    (a) 9 − 6 = ☐ (b) 8 − 3 = ☐

    90 − 60 = ☐   80 − 30 = ☐

    900 − 600 = ☐   800 − 300 = ☐

    (c) 8 6 9   (d) 7 6 5   (e) 6 4 5
       − 2 6   − 5 3   − 4 0 5
       ―――――   ―――――   ―――――

    (f) 6 7 0   (g) 7 8 9   (h) 6 5 8
       − 4 2 0   − 4 5 7   − 5 5 2
       ―――――   ―――――   ―――――

    (i) 8 0 9   (j) 5 6 5   (k) 9 3 4
       − 8 0 3   − 5 2 5   − 7 3 2
       ―――――   ―――――   ―――――

2. Fill in the boxes.

(a) 496 − 80 = ☐ (b) 598 − 75 = ☐
(c) 368 − 67 = ☐ (d) 276 − 200 = ☐
(e) 956 − 246 = ☐ (f) 885 − 860 = ☐
(g) 752 − 542 = ☐ (h) 918 − 905 = ☐

3. Fill in the blanks.

(a) Subtract 24 from 78. The answer is _____.

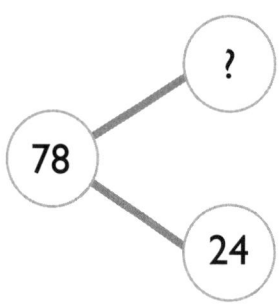

(b) Subtract 35 from 99. The answer is _____.

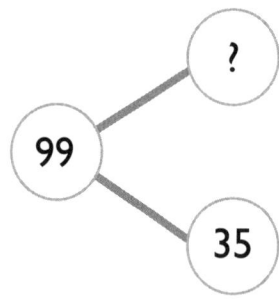

(c) Subtract 64 from 796. The answer is _____.

(d) Subtract 217 from 729. The answer is _____.

(e) Subtract 356 from 958. The answer is _____.

4. Solve.

(a) There are 294 cars in a parking lot.
52 of them are new cars.
How many old cars are there?

There are _____ old cars.

(b) A fruit seller has 566 oranges and 243 pears. How many more oranges than pears does he have?

The fruit seller has _____ more oranges than pears.

(c) A shopkeeper sold 659 pens. He sold 53 more pens than pencils. How many pencils did he sell?

The shopkeeper sold _____ pencils.

Exercise 4A : Addition With Renaming

1. Add.

    (a) $6 + 4 = \boxed{}$ (b) $4 + 8 = \boxed{}$

    $60 + 40 = \boxed{}$ $84 + 8 = \boxed{}$

    $760 + 40 = \boxed{}$ $884 + 8 = \boxed{}$

    (c) $9 + 7 = \boxed{}$ (d) $5 + 6 = \boxed{}$

    $90 + 70 = \boxed{}$ $35 + 6 = \boxed{}$

    $590 + 70 = \boxed{}$ $635 + 6 = \boxed{}$

    (e) $7 + 6 = \boxed{}$ (f) $7 + 8 = \boxed{}$

    $57 + 6 = \boxed{}$ $87 + 8 = \boxed{}$

    $457 + 6 = \boxed{}$ $687 + 8 = \boxed{}$

2. Add.

    (a) $56 + 6 = \boxed{}$ (b) $83 + 9 = \boxed{}$

    (c) $167 + 7 = \boxed{}$ (d) $562 + 8 = \boxed{}$

    (e) $280 + 60 = \boxed{}$ (f) $470 + 80 = \boxed{}$

    (g) $370 + 30 = \boxed{}$ (h) $760 + 90 = \boxed{}$

3. Add.

(a) 526 + 66

(b) 329 + 145

(c) 607 + 78

(d) 536 + 259

(e) 583 + 84

(f) 376 + 473

(g) 330 + 570

(h) 682 + 275

4. Solve.

(a) Store A sold 685 toy soldiers.
Store A sold 53 fewer toy soldiers than Store B.
How many toy soldiers did Store B sell?

Store B sold _____ toy soldiers.

(b) A man sold 530 balloons on Saturday.
He sold 295 more balloons on Sunday than on Saturday. How many balloons did he sell on Sunday?

The man sold _____ balloons on Sunday.

Exercise 4B : Addition With Renaming

1. Add.

(a) 685 + 47

(b) 365 + 78

(c) 697 + 86

(d) 539 + 276

(e)

(f)

(g) 54 + 37 + 76 + 98

(h) 34 + 29 + 66 + 82

178 + 189

284 + 367

(i) 23 + 38 + 42 + 79

(j) 560 + 145 + 44

(k) 398 + 78 + 112

(l) 536 + 198 + 65

(m) 344 + 158 + 467

(n) 153 + 264 + 439

(o) 256 + 383 + 182

(p) 168 + 375 + 396

2. Solve.

   (a) After selling 189 shirts, a shopkeeper had 78 shirts left.
   How many shirts did he have at first?

   The shopkeeper had _____ shirts at first.

   (b) The chart below shows the number of people at a party.
   How many people were there at the party?

Men	175
Women	66
Children	226

   There were _____ people at the party.

   (c) The table shows the points earned by Alan.
   What are his total points for the three subjects?

English	83
Mathematics	76
Science	92

   Alan's total points for the three subjects are _____.

Exercise 5A : Subtraction With Renaming

1. Subtract.

   (a)   53
       − 37
       ____

   (b)   75
       − 46
       ____

   (c)   81
       − 56
       ____

   (d)   96
       − 58
       ____

   (e)   64
       − 38
       ____

   (f)   87
       − 69
       ____

   (g)   80
       − 74
       ____

   (h)   92
       − 85
       ____

   (i)   875
       − 248
       ____

   (j)   763
       − 49
       ____

   (k)   804
       − 63
       ____

   (l)   881
       − 567
       ____

   (m)   682
       − 575
       ____

   (n)   394
       − 136
       ____

   (o)   933
       − 271
       ____

   (p)   654
       − 564
       ____

2. Solve.

(a) Sam had 235 puzzle pieces.
He fit 52 pieces together.
How many more pieces did he have to fit together?

Sam had _____ more pieces to fit together.

(b) Brenna collected 68 postcards.
Her brother collected 129 postcards.
How many fewer postcards did Brenna collect?

Brenna collected _____ fewer postcards.

(c) Diane has $236.
She wants to buy a bicycle that costs $354.
How much more money does she need?

Diane needs $_____ more.

Exercise 5B : Subtraction With Renaming

1. Subtract.

   (a)   3 0 5   (b)   5 0 7   (c)   6 0 6   (d)   9 0 5
       −   2 7   −   8 8   −   7 8   −   5 7
       ―――――   ―――――   ―――――   ―――――

   (e)   4 0 2   (f)   6 0 8   (g)   7 0 7   (h)   8 0 4
       − 1 2 8   − 2 4 9   − 4 1 9   − 7 9 8
       ―――――   ―――――   ―――――   ―――――

   (i)   2 0 0   (j)   4 0 0   (k)   8 0 0   (l)   9 0 0
       −   7 5   −   9 8   −   4 6   −   2 3
       ―――――   ―――――   ―――――   ―――――

   (m)   5 0 0   (n)   6 0 0   (o)   7 0 0   (p)   8 0 0
       − 2 6 8   − 3 9 7   − 6 3 4   − 7 9 2
       ―――――   ―――――   ―――――   ―――――

2. Solve.

   (a) Taylor went shopping with $500.
       After shopping, she had $252 left.
       How much money did she spend?

       Taylor spent $_____.

   (b) There are 356 trees in Town A.
       There are 704 trees in Town B.
       How many more trees are there in Town B than in Town A?

       There are _____ more trees in Town B than in Town A.

   (c) Mr. Ray sold 600 flowers on Saturday.
       He sold 293 fewer flowers on Sunday than on Saturday.
       How many flowers did he sell on Sunday?

       Mr. Ray sold _____ flowers on Sunday.

Unit 3 : Length

Friendly Notes

We can use things like paper clips and footprints to measure length.

Measure the rod.

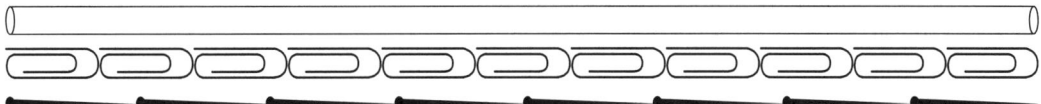

The rod is about 11 ⊂⊃ long.

The rod is about 8 •— long.

We can also measure length in centimeters and inches.
We write **cm** for centimeter and **in**. for inch.
We usually use **cm** and **in**. for measuring short lengths.

1 inch > 1 cm

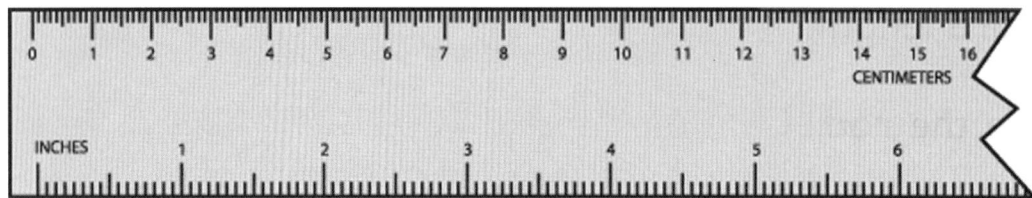

Measure the pencil and the rod.

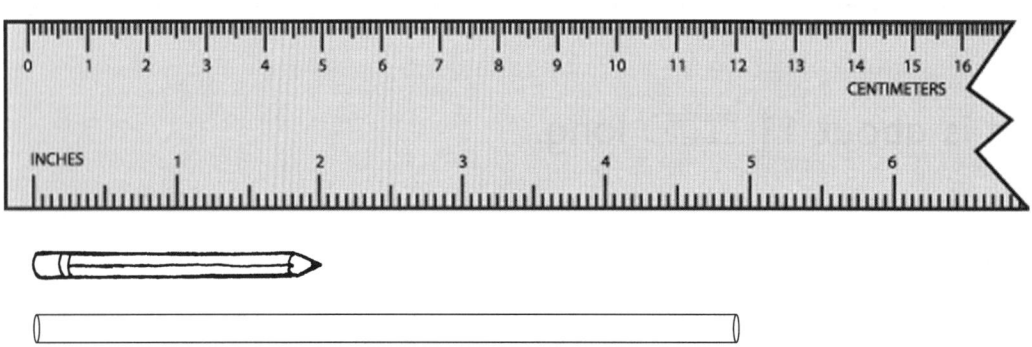

We usually measure things starting with the mark under '0' on the ruler.

The pencil is 5 cm long or about 2 inches long.

The rod is 12 cm long or about 5 inches long.

The meter, feet, and yard are other units for measuring length.
They are used for measuring longer lengths.
We write **m** for meter, **ft** for foot or feet, and **yd** for yard.

1 yard is a little shorter than 1 meter.

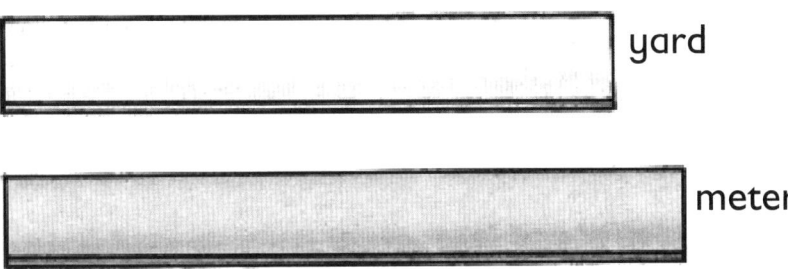

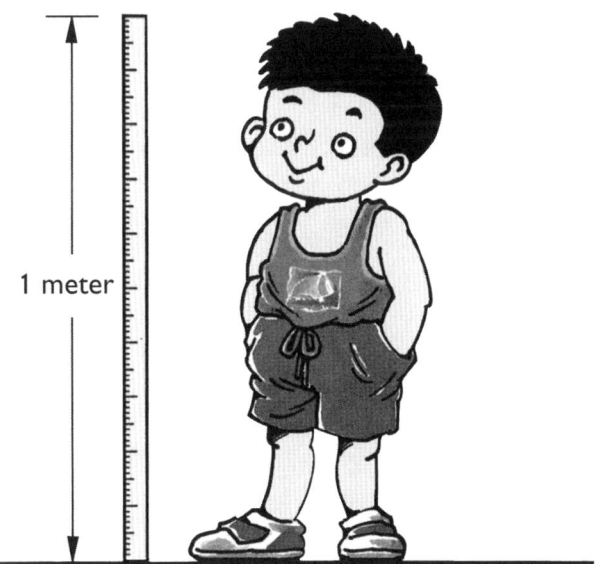

The boy is 1 m tall.

1 meter = 100 centimeters
1 yard = 3 feet
1 foot = 12 inches

3. The length of a table is 2 yd.
   (a) Is the length more than, less than, or the same as 2 ft?
   (b) Is the length more than, less than, or the same as 2 m?

   (a) 1 yd = 3 ft
   2 yd is more than 3 ft.

   The length is more than 2 ft.

   (b) 1 yd is a little shorter than 1 m.
   2 yd is shorter than 2 m.

   The length is less than 2 m.

Exercise 1 : Measuring Length

1. Fill in the blanks.

(a) The book is about _____ 🖍 long.

(b) The book is about _____ 🖍 long.

(c) The whiteboard is about _____ 🖍 long.

(d) The whiteboard is about _____ 🖍 long.

(e) The whiteboard is longer than the _____.

(f) The book is shorter than the _____.

2. Fill in the blanks.

Stick A

Stick B

Stick C

(a) Stick A is _____ handprints long.

(b) Stick B is _____ handprints long.

(c) Stick C is _____ handprints long.

(d) Stick A is longer than Stick _____.

(e) Stick _____ is 1 handprint longer than Stick _____.

(f) Stick A is shorter than Stick _____.

(g) Stick _____ is 3 handprints shorter than Stick _____.

(h) Stick _____ is the longest.

Exercise 2 : Measuring Length in Meters

1. Measure the following with a measuring tape. Write **Yes** or **No** in the boxes.

   (a)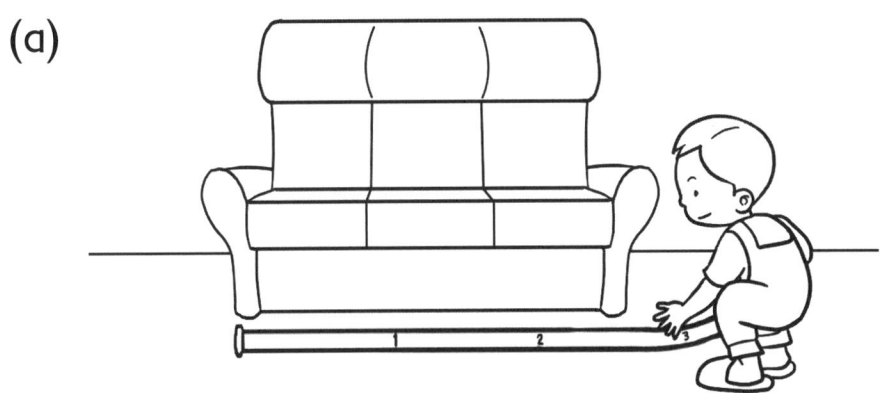

   Is the length of the sofa more than 3 m?

   ☐

   (b)

   Is the length of the window less than 2 m?

   ☐

2. Solve.

   (a) Lily is running in a 100-meter race. She is 32 m from the finishing point. How many meters is she from the starting point?

   Lily is _____ m from the starting point.

   (b)

   Daniel and Ryan walk to school every day. How much farther does Ryan walk than Daniel?

   Ryan walks _____ m farther than Daniel.

Exercise 3 : Measuring Length in Centimeters

1. Fill in the blanks.

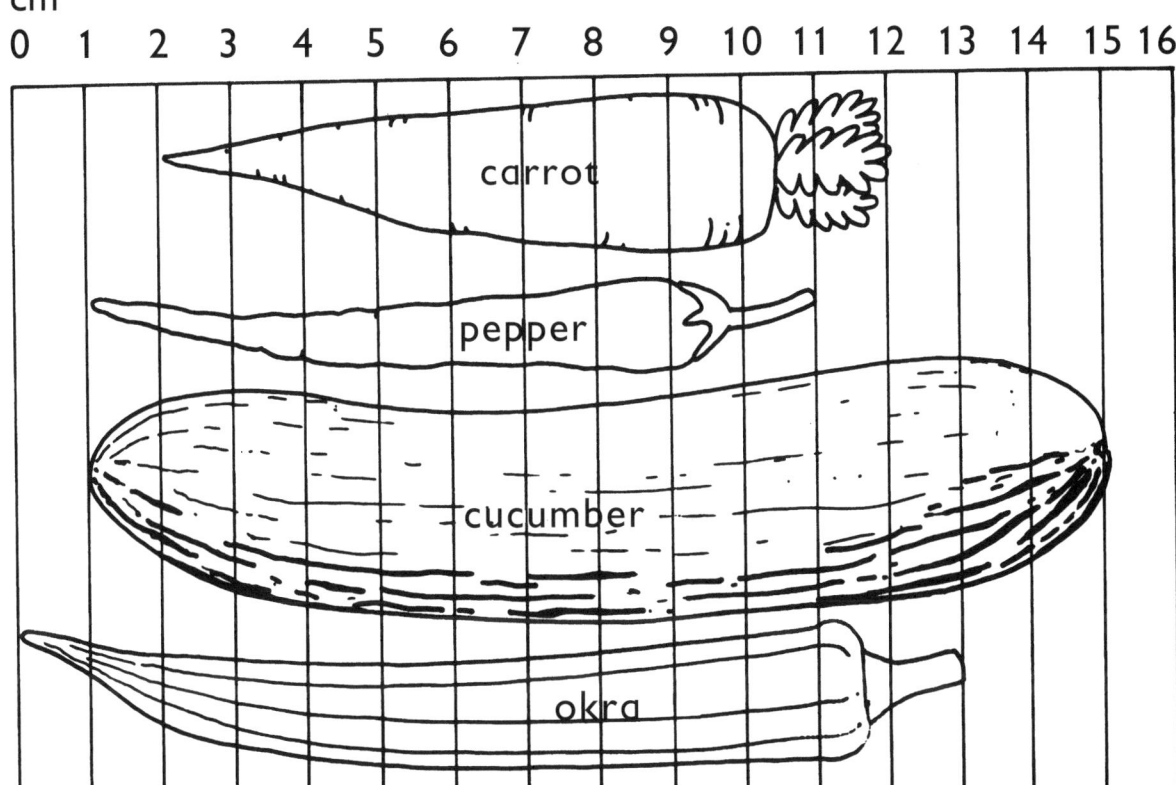

(a) The carrot is _____ cm long.

(b) The pepper is _____ cm long.

(c) The cucumber is _____ cm long.

(d) The pepper is _____ cm shorter than the cucumber.

(e) The okra is _____ cm longer than the carrot.

2. Use a string and a ruler to measure these lines.

(a) Line A is about _____ cm long.

(b) Line B is about _____ cm long.

(c) Line _____ is longer than Line _____.

3. Using your ruler, draw two lines.

Line C : 4 cm

Line D : 7 cm

Line _____ is shorter than Line _____.

Name: _____ Class: _____ Date: _____

Exercise 4 : Other Units of Length

1. Measure the following with a yard stick.
   Check (✓) the correct box in the table.

	Less than 1 yd	More than 1 yd
My friend's height		
Height of door		
Height of my chair		
Length of window		

2. Measure the following with a ruler.
   Write **Yes** or **No** in the boxes.

   (a) Is the length of your textbook more than 1 ft?

   (b) Is the length of your foot less than 1 ft?

3. Circle the correct answer.

   Whitney's room is 4 yd long.

   Whitney's room is (more than, less than, the same as) 4 ft long.

4. Solve.

(a) After using 46 yd of wire, Peter had 74 yd of wire left. How many yards of wire did he have at first?

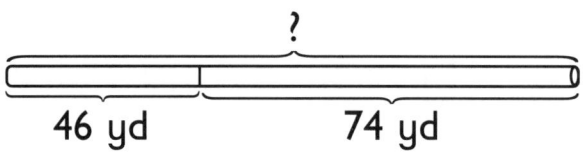

Peter had _____ yd of wire at first.

(b) Mrs. Felipe bought 132 yd of material to make curtains. She used 34 yd of material. How many yards of material did she have left?

Mrs. Felipe had _____ yd of material left.

5. Fill in the blanks.

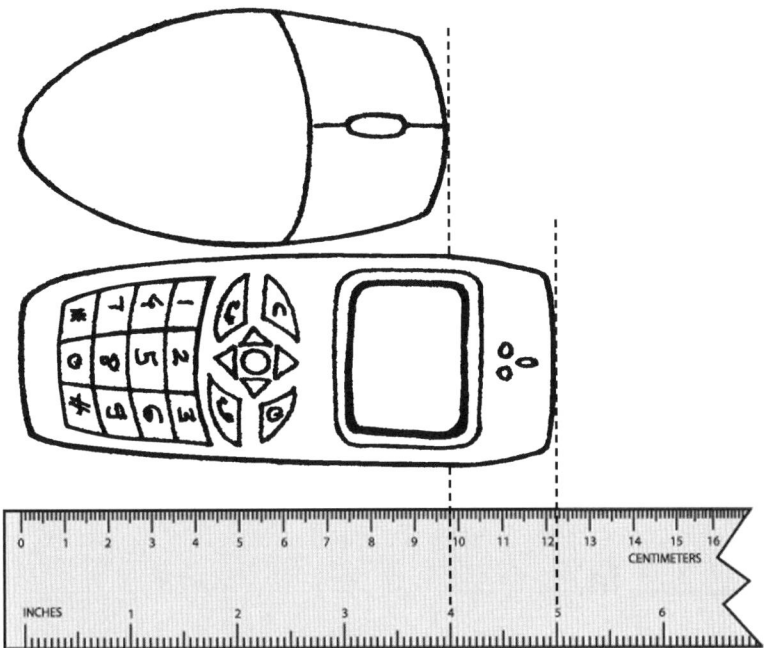

(a) The computer mouse is _____ in. long.

(b) The cellphone is _____ in. long.

(c) The computer mouse is _____ in. shorter than the cellphone.

(d) The cellphone is _____ in. longer than the computer mouse.

6. Use your ruler to measure the following in inches and fill in the blanks.

   (a) The thickness of my workbook is about _____ in.

   (b) The length of my pencil is about _____ in.

   (c) The length of my pencil case is about _____ in.

   (d) The width of my notebook is about _____ in.

7. Use your ruler to measure the following lines in inches and fill in the blanks.

   Line A ─────────────

   Line B ──────────────────────

   (a) Line A is _____ in. long.

   (b) Line B is _____ in. long.

   (c) Line B is _____ in. longer than Line A.

8. Write **Yes** or **No** in the box.

   John's table is 5 ft long.

   Is John's table more than 12 in.?   ☐

Unit 4 : Multiplication and Division

Friendly Notes

Multiplication

We multiply to find the total when equal groups are put together.

There are 5 tomatoes on 1 plate.
There are 3 plates.

3 groups of 5 = 3 fives
$= 5 + 5 + 5 = 15$

We write the multiplication equation:
3 × 5 = 15

There are 3 groups of 5 tomatoes.

We can also write:
5 × 3 = 15

There are 5 tomatoes on each of the 3 plates.

There are **15** tomatoes altogether.

Division

We share equally or put things into equal groups when we divide.
We divide to find the number in each equal group.

1. Share 6 bananas equally between 2 monkeys.
   How many bananas does each monkey get?

   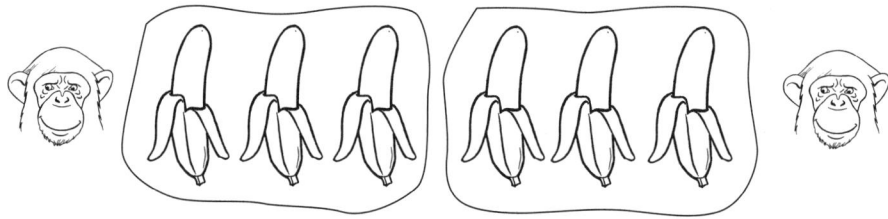

   We write the division equation:

   $6 \div 2 = 3$

   Each monkey gets 3 bananas.

We also divide to find the number of equal groups.

2. Divide 10 apples into groups of 5.
   How many equal groups are there?

   We write the division equation:

   $10 \div 5 = 2$

   There are 2 equal groups.

Exercise 1 : Multiplication

1. Fill in the boxes and blanks.

    (a)

    3 fours = ☐ + ☐ + ☐ = ☐

    3 × 4 = ☐

    (b)

    4 threes = ☐ + ☐ + ☐ + ☐ = ☐

    4 × 3 = ☐

    (c)

    4 fives = ☐ + ☐ + ☐ + ☐ = ☐

    4 × 5 = ☐

(d)

2 groups of 9 = ☐

2 × 9 = ☐

(e)

9 groups of 2 = ☐

9 × 2 = ☐

(f)

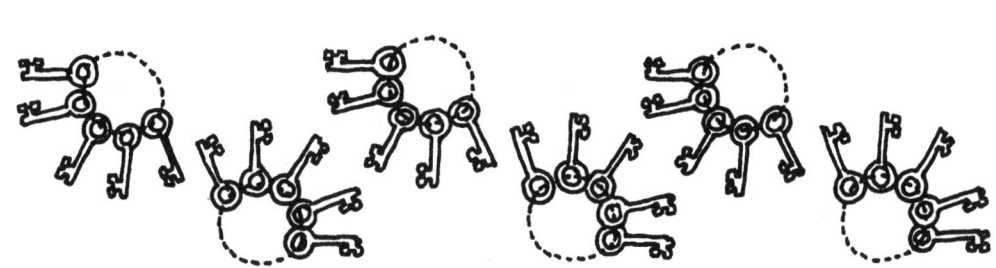

6 groups of 5 = ☐

6 × 5 = ☐

(g) Multiply 2 by 7.

2 + 2 + 2 + 2 + 2 + 2 + 2 = ☐

2 × 7 = ☐

There are _____ flowers altogether.

(h) Multiply 7 by 2.

7 + 7 = ☐

7 × 2 = ☐

There are _____ flowers altogether.

(i) Multiply 6 by 4.

6 × 4 = ☐

There are _____ stars altogether.

(j) There are 4 cakes in one box.
How many cakes are there in 6 boxes?

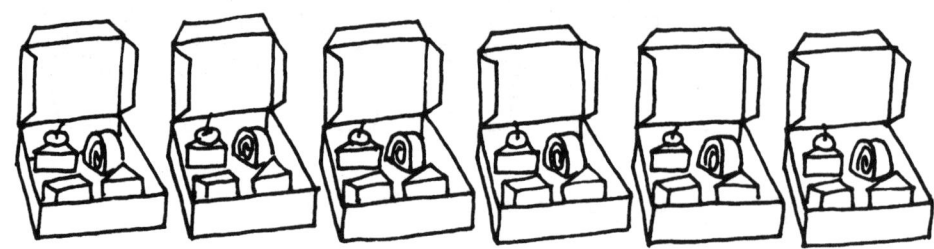

☐ × ☐ = ☐

There are _____ cakes altogether.

(k) There are 8 pears on one plate.
How many pears are there on 3 plates?

☐ × ☐ = ☐

There are _____ pears altogether.

(l) An ant has 6 legs.
How many legs do 3 ants have?

☐ × ☐ = ☐

3 ants have _____ legs.

2. Complete the multiplication equations.

(a)

4 × 10 = ☐   10 × 4 = ☐

(b)

6 × 3 = ☐   3 × 6 = ☐

(c)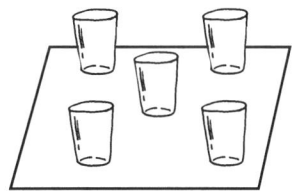

2 × 5 = ☐   ☐ × 2 = ☐

(d)

7 × 3 = ☐   3 × ☐ = ☐

3. Write two multiplication equations for each of the following.

(a)

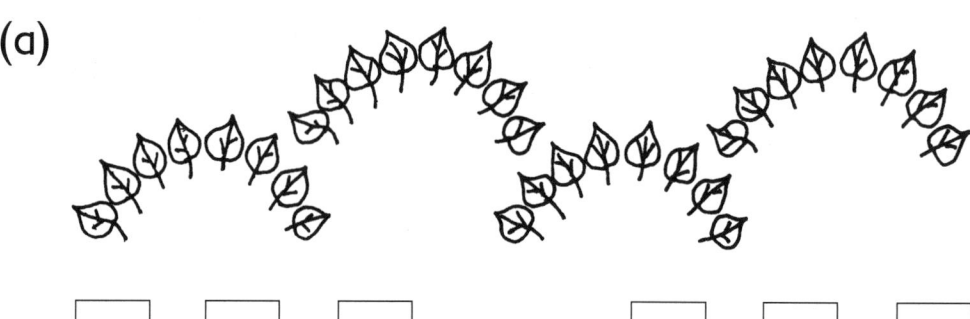

☐ × ☐ = ☐   ☐ × ☐ = ☐

(b)

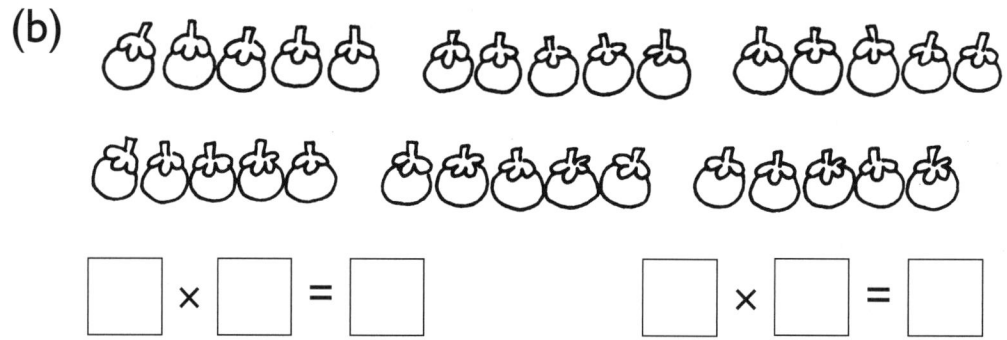

☐ × ☐ = ☐   ☐ × ☐ = ☐

(c)

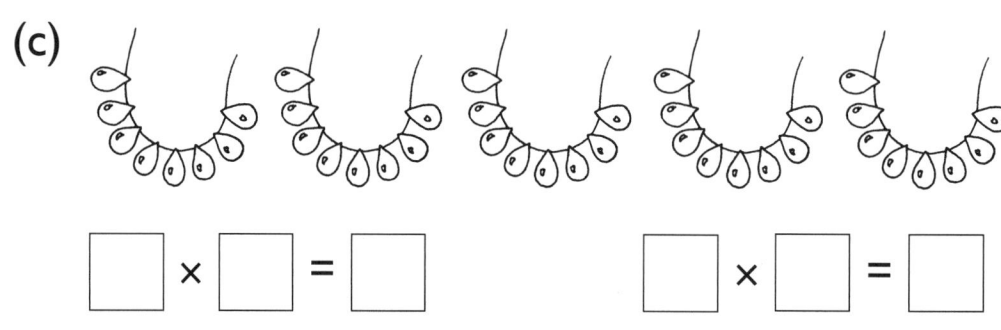

☐ × ☐ = ☐   ☐ × ☐ = ☐

(d)

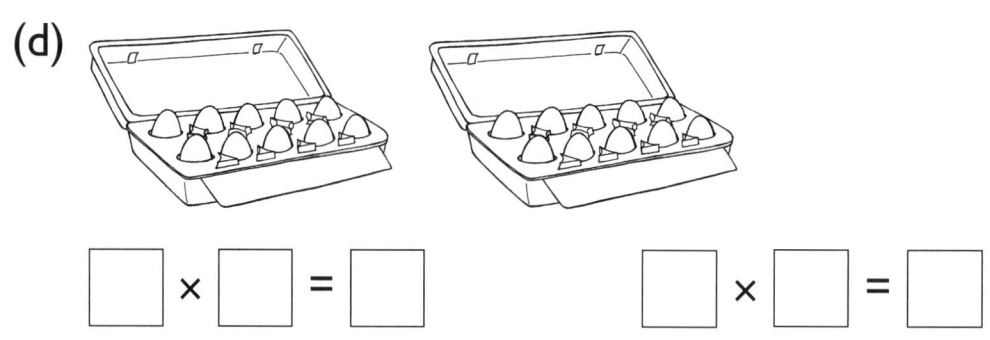

☐ × ☐ = ☐   ☐ × ☐ = ☐

Exercise 2 : Division

1. Fill in the blanks and boxes.

   (a) Divide 15 apples into 3 equal groups.

   There are _____ apples in each group.

   (b) Divide 24 marbles into 4 equal groups.

   There are _____ marbles in each group.

   (c) Divide 20 keys into 5 equal groups.

   There are _____ keys in each group.

   (d) Divide 18 caps into 3 equal groups.

   $18 \div 3 = \boxed{}$

   There are _____ caps in each group.

(e) Divide 16 birds into groups of 4.

16 ÷ 4 = ☐

There are _____ groups.

(f) Divide 21 cups into groups of 3.

21 ÷ 3 = ☐

There are _____ groups.

(g) Divide 30 chicks into groups of 5.

30 ÷ 5 = ☐

There are _____ groups.

2. Complete the division equations.

   (a)

   $28 \div 4 = \boxed{}$ $28 \div 7 = \boxed{}$

   (b)

   $32 \div 4 = \boxed{}$ $32 \div 8 = \boxed{}$

   (c)

   $18 \div 2 = \boxed{}$ $18 \div 9 = \boxed{}$

3. Write two division equations.

(a)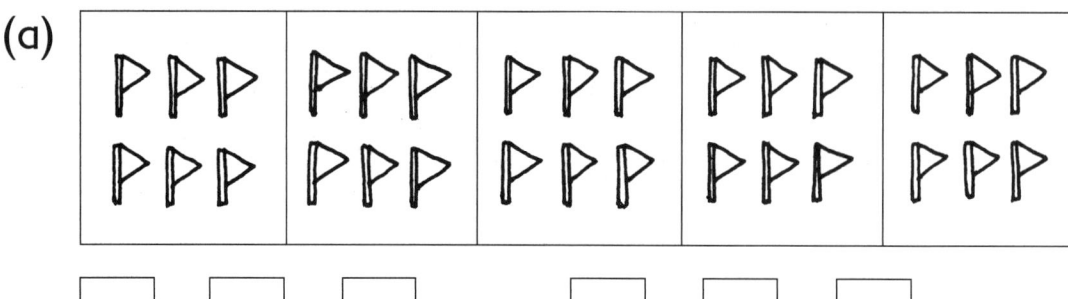

(b)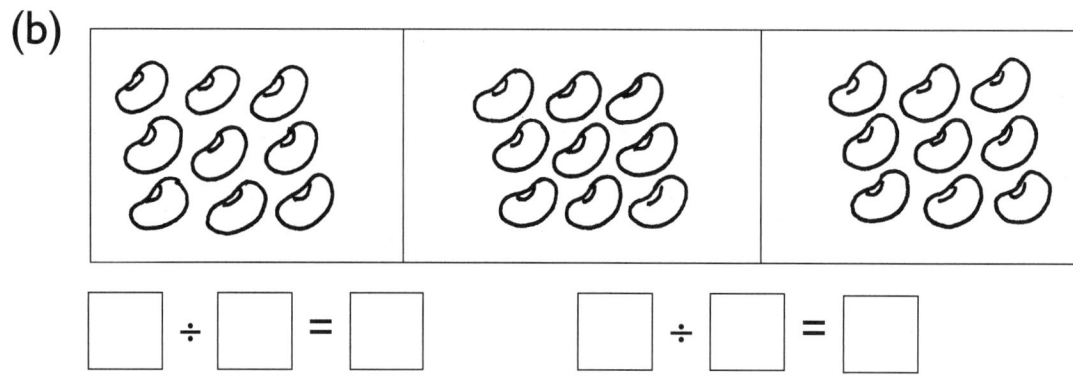

☐ ÷ ☐ = ☐   ☐ ÷ ☐ = ☐

4. Write two multiplication equations and two division equations.

☐ × ☐ = ☐   ☐ × ☐ = ☐

☐ ÷ ☐ = ☐   ☐ ÷ ☐ = ☐

5. Solve.
   (a) Mary uses 3 straws to make 1 triangle.
       How many triangles can she make with 24 straws?

   □ ○ □ = □

   Mary can make _____ triangles with 24 straws.

   (b) 6 boys share 24 balloons equally.
       How many balloons does each boy get?

   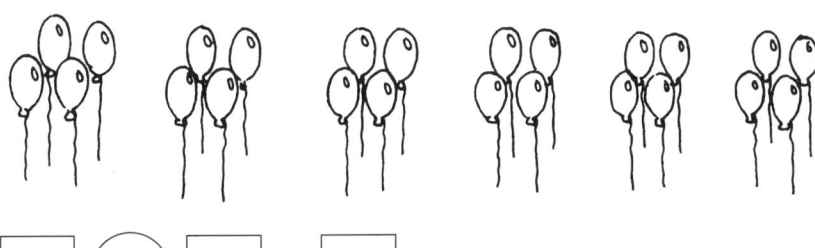

   □ ○ □ = □

   Each boy gets _____ balloons.

   (c) Kathy tied 20 flowers into bunches of 5.
       How many bunches were there?

   □ ○ □ = □

   There were _____ bunches.

(d) 5 rabbits share 15 carrots equally.
How many carrots does each rabbit get?

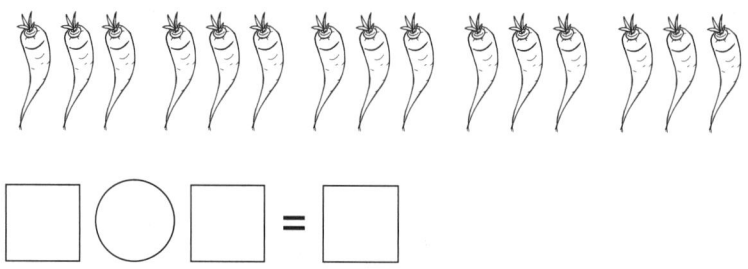

☐ ◯ ☐ = ☐

Each rabbit gets _____ carrots.

(e) Rita put 12 cups of tea equally onto 3 trays.
How many cups of tea did she put on each tray?

☐ ◯ ☐ = ☐

Rita put _____ cups of tea on each tray.

(f) John has 20 toy planes.
He packs 10 toy planes in each box.
How many boxes did John use?

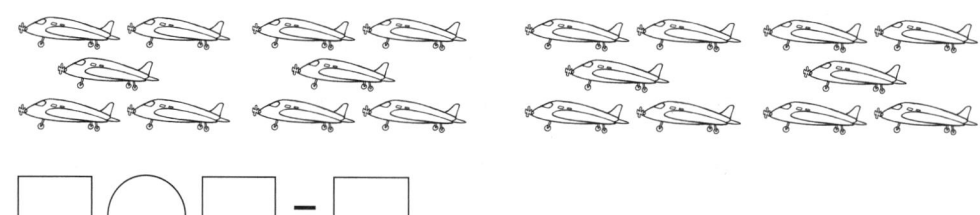

☐ ◯ ☐ = ☐

John used _____ boxes.

Unit 5 : Multiplication Tables of 2 and 3

Friendly Notes

Multiplication Table of 2

We can count by 2's to help us remember the multiplication table of 2.

$1 \times 2 = 2$	◯◯
$2 \times 2 = 4$	◯◯ ◯◯
$3 \times 2 = 6$	◯◯ ◯◯ ◯◯
$4 \times 2 = 8$	◯◯ ◯◯ ◯◯ ◯◯
$5 \times 2 = 10$	◯◯ ◯◯ ◯◯ ◯◯ ◯◯
$6 \times 2 = 12$	◯◯ ◯◯ ◯◯ ◯◯ ◯◯ ◯◯
$7 \times 2 = 14$	◯◯ ◯◯ ◯◯ ◯◯ ◯◯ ◯◯ ◯◯
$8 \times 2 = 16$	◯◯ ◯◯ ◯◯ ◯◯ ◯◯ ◯◯ ◯◯ ◯◯
$9 \times 2 = 18$	◯◯ ◯◯ ◯◯ ◯◯ ◯◯ ◯◯ ◯◯ ◯◯ ◯◯
$10 \times 2 = 20$	◯◯ ◯◯ ◯◯ ◯◯ ◯◯ ◯◯ ◯◯ ◯◯ ◯◯ ◯◯

Multiplication Table of 3

We can count by 3's to help us remember the multiplication table of 3.

1 × 3 = **3**	
2 × 3 = **6**	
3 × 3 = **9**	
4 × 3 = **12**	
5 × 3 = **15**	
6 × 3 = **18**	
7 × 3 = **21**	
8 × 3 = **24**	
9 × 3 = **27**	
10 × 3 = **30**	

Dividing by 2
We can divide by 2 using multiplication facts.

1 × 2 = 2	2 ÷ 2 = 1
2 × 2 = 4	4 ÷ 2 = 2
3 × 2 = 6	6 ÷ 2 = 3
4 × 2 = 8	8 ÷ 2 = 4
5 × 2 = 10	10 ÷ 2 = 5
6 × 2 = 12	12 ÷ 2 = 6
7 × 2 = 14	14 ÷ 2 = 7
8 × 2 = 16	16 ÷ 2 = 8
9 × 2 = 18	18 ÷ 2 = 9
10 × 2 = 20	20 ÷ 2 = 10

Dividing by 3
We can divide by 3 using multiplication facts.

1 × 3 = 3	3 ÷ 3 = 1
2 × 3 = 6	6 ÷ 3 = 2
3 × 3 = 9	9 ÷ 3 = 3
4 × 3 = 12	12 ÷ 3 = 4
5 × 3 = 15	15 ÷ 3 = 5
6 × 3 = 18	18 ÷ 3 = 6
7 × 3 = 21	21 ÷ 3 = 7
8 × 3 = 24	24 ÷ 3 = 8
9 × 3 = 27	27 ÷ 3 = 9
10 × 3 = 30	30 ÷ 3 = 10

Division with Remainder

> We get a remainder when we cannot divide a number exactly.

Divide 17 marbles between 2 children.

(a) How many marbles does each child get?
(b) How many marbles are left over?

$2 \times 8 = 16$
$2 \times 9 = 18$
There are only 17 marbles.
So each child gets 8 marbles.
$17 - 16 = 1$

$17 \div 2 = 8$ with 1 left over

(a) Each child gets 8 marbles.
(b) 1 marble is left over.

Exercise 1 : Multiplication Table of 2

1. Match.

5 × 2	6	2 × 6
8 × 2	10	2 × 3
3 × 2	12	2 × 5
6 × 2	16	2 × 4
10 × 2	8	2 × 9
4 × 2	14	2 × 8
9 × 2	20	2 × 7
7 × 2	18	2 × 10

2. Match.

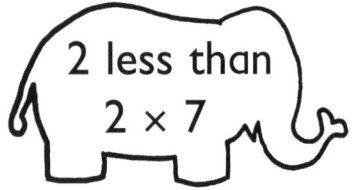  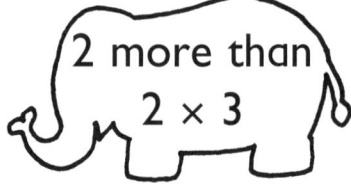

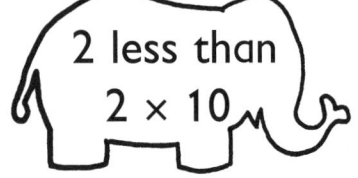  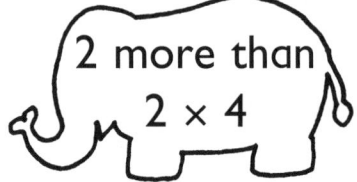

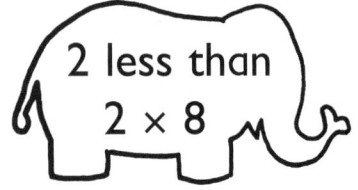  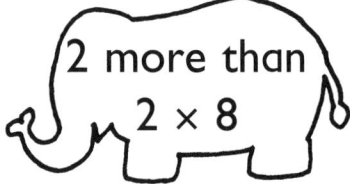

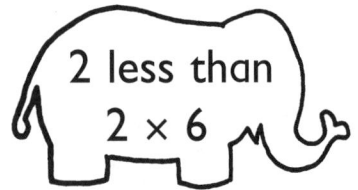  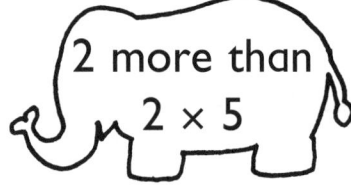

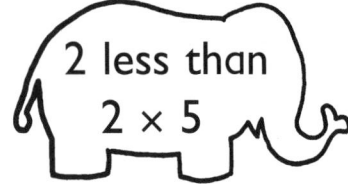  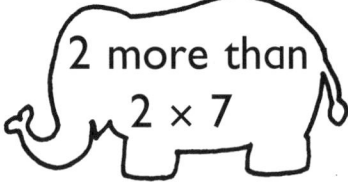

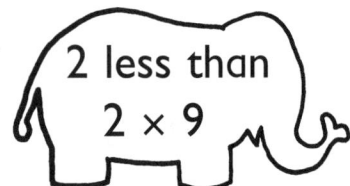 

3. Complete the multiplication equations.

(a)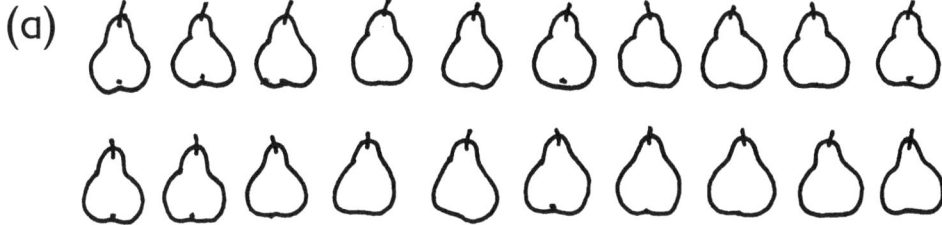

$2 \times 10 =$ ☐
$10 \times 2 =$ ☐

(b)

$2 \times 8 =$ ☐
$8 \times 2 =$ ☐

(c)

$2 \times 9 =$ ☐
$9 \times 2 =$ ☐

4. Check (✓) if the equation is correct.

(a)	$6 \times 2 = 2 \times 6$	
(b)	$4 \times 2 = 4 + 4$	
(c)	$7 \times 2 = 2 + 7$	
(d)	$5 \times 2 = 2 + 2 + 2 + 2$	

5. Solve.
   (a) Justin bought 2 books.
   Each book cost $7.
   How much did he pay altogether?

   Justin paid _____ altogether.

   (b) There are 2 birds in one cage.
   How many birds are there in 9 such cages?

   There are _____ birds in 9 cages.

   (c) Hannah uses 2 m of cloth to make one shirt.
   How many meters of cloth does she use to make 10 shirts?

   Hannah uses _____ m of cloth.

Exercise 2 : Multiplication Table of 3

1. Match.

  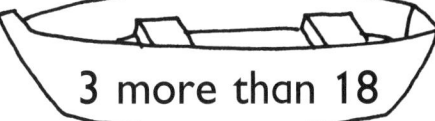

  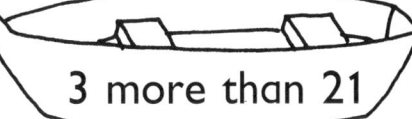

3×6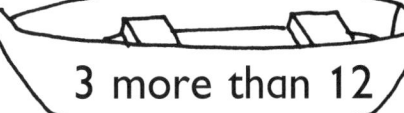

3×8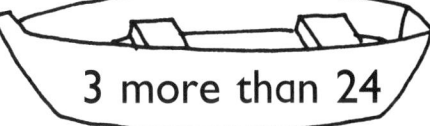

3×4

2. Match.

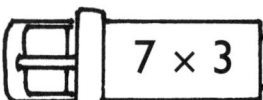  3 × 4

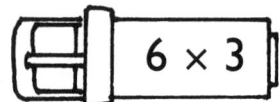 27 3 × 8

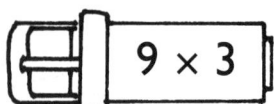 12 3 × 6

4 × 3 24 3 × 5

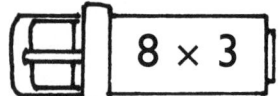  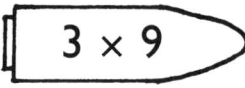

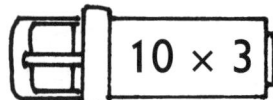  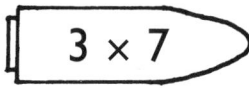

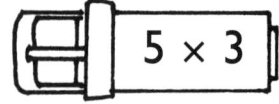  3 × 2

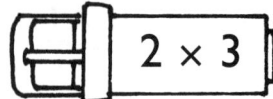  3 × 10

3. Complete the multiplication equations.

(a)

$3 \times 5 =$ ☐

$5 \times 3 =$ ☐

(b)

$3 \times 8 =$ ☐

$8 \times 3 =$ ☐

(c)

$3 \times 7 =$ ☐

$7 \times 3 =$ ☐

(d)

$3 \times 6 =$ ☐

$6 \times 3 =$ ☐

(e)

$3 \times 9 =$ ☐

$9 \times 3 =$ ☐

4. Complete the table.

(a)

	1	3	5	2	4	6	7	9	10	8
× 2	2	6	10							
× 3	3	9								

(b) A rabbit has 2 ears.

Number of rabbits	1	3	5	7	8	9
Number of ears	2					

(c) A stool has 3 legs.

Number of stools	1	3	5	7	8	9
Number of legs	3					

5. Check (✓) if the equation is correct.

(a)	3 × 8 = 8 + 8 + 8	
(b)	3 × 4 = 4 × 3	
(c)	6 × 3 = 6 + 3 + 6 + 3	

6. Solve.

   (a) Mark saves $3 a week.
       How much can he save in 5 weeks?

       Mark can save $_____ in 5 weeks.

   (b) A monkey eats 3 bananas a day.
       How many bananas does it eat in a week?

       The monkey eats _____ bananas in a week.

   (c) Kyle sold 3 pencils a day.
       How many pencils did he sell in 10 days?

       Kyle sold _____ pencils in 10 days.

(d) Rebecca bought 3 yd of cloth.
1 yd of cloth cost $9.
How much did she pay?

Rebecca paid $_____.

(e) Javier bought a bag of sugar for $3.
How much did he pay for 6 bags of sugar?

Javier paid $_____ for 6 bags of sugar.

(f) 3 apples cost $1.
Paul paid $8.
How many apples did he buy?

Paul bought _____ apples.

Exercise 3 : Dividing by 2

1. Match.

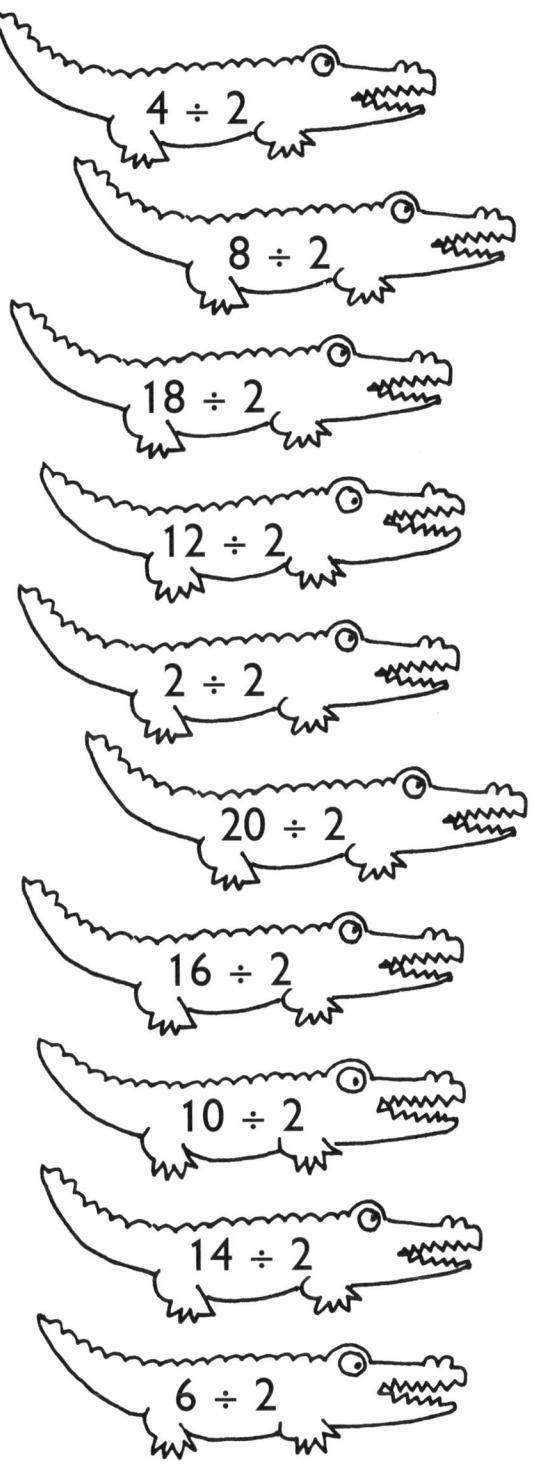 

2. Fill in the boxes.

(a)
$5 \times 2 = 10$
$10 \div 2 = \boxed{}$

(b)
$7 \times 2 = 14$
$14 \div 2 = \boxed{}$

(c)
$\boxed{} \times 2 = 12$
$12 \div 2 = \boxed{}$

(d)
$\boxed{} \times 2 = 18$
$18 \div 2 = \boxed{}$

(e)
$\boxed{} \times 2 = 8$
$8 \div 2 = \boxed{}$

(f)
$\boxed{} \times 2 = 16$
$16 \div 2 = \boxed{}$

3. Solve.
   (a) Siti had a string 8 m long.
       She cut it into 2 equal pieces.
       What was the length of each piece?

       The length of each piece was _____ m.

   (b) Mary saved $2 a week.
       How many weeks did she take to save $16?

       Mary took _____ weeks to save $16.

   (c) Tyrone puts 12 oranges equally into 2 bags.
       How many oranges are there in each bag?

       There are _____ oranges in each bag.

(d) David and his sister shared $20 equally.
How much money did each of them get?

Each of them got $_____.

(e) Mr. Coles put 14 students into 2 equal groups.
How many students were there in each group?

There were _____ students in each group.

(f) Matthew sold 18 umbrellas in 2 days.
He sold the same number of umbrellas each day.
How many umbrellas did he sell each day?

Matthew sold _____ umbrellas each day.

Exercise 4 : Dividing by 3

1. Match.

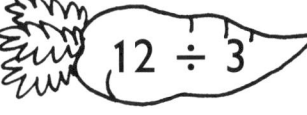

 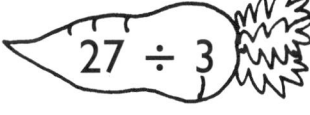 

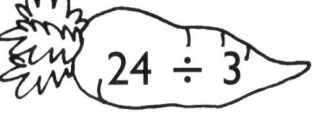

2. Fill in the boxes.

(a)

5 × 3 = 15

15 ÷ 3 = ☐

(b)

3 × 3 = 9

9 ÷ 3 = ☐

(c)

7 × 3 = 21

21 ÷ 3 = ☐

(d)

10 × 3 = 30

30 ÷ 3 = ☐

(e)

8 × 3 = 24

24 ÷ 3 = ☐

(f)

6 × 3 = 18

18 ÷ 3 = ☐

3. Solve.
   (a) Mr. King arranged 24 desks equally in 3 rows. How many desks were there in each row?

   There were _____ desks in each row.

   (b) 3 DVDS cost $27.
       What is the cost of 1 DVD?

   The cost of 1 DVD is $_____.

   (c) The total length of 3 equal pieces of wire is 21 in. What is the length of each piece of wire?

   The length of each piece of wire is _____ in.

(d) A girl used 3 m of ribbon to tie a package.
If she used 18 m of ribbon altogether,
how many packages did she tie?

The girl tied _____ packages.

(e) 3 oranges cost $1.
Kevin bought 18 oranges.
How much did he pay?

Kevin paid $_____.

(f) Ashley's mother bought 12 towels.
Ashley and her two brothers shared the
towels equally.
How many towels did each of them get?

Each of them got _____ towels.

Exercise 5 : Remainders

1. Fill in the blanks.
   The clown has 20 balloons.
   He gives 3 balloons to each child.
   (a) How many children get the balloons?
   (b) How many balloons are left over?

20 ÷ 3 is _____ with _____ left over.

(a) _____ children get the balloons.

(b) _____ balloons are left over.

2. Solve.
   (a) Uma has 11 pencils.
   She shares them equally with her sister.
   How many pencils are left over?

   (b) George arranges 9 toy cars in rows of 2 each.
   (i) How many rows of toy cars are there?
   (ii) Find the remaining number of toy cars.

Unit 6 : Addition and Subtraction

Friendly Notes

Finding the Missing Number

We add to find the whole.
We subtract to find one part.

1. Find the missing number.

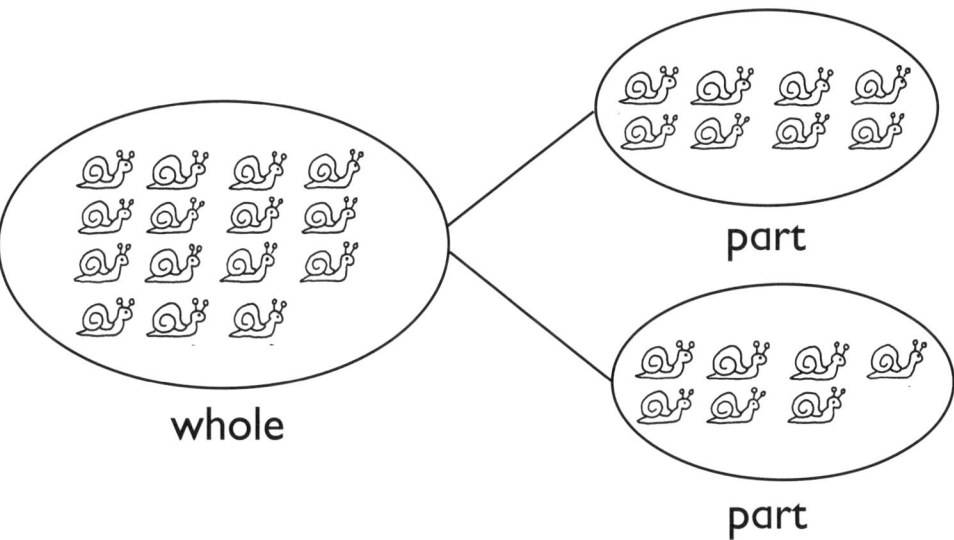

$7 + 8 = 15$

part part whole

$15 - \boxed{8} = 7$

To find one part, we subtract.
$15 - 7 = 8$
$15 - \boxed{8} = 7$

2. Find the missing number.

   $\boxed{14} - 9 = 5$

   To find the whole, we add.
   $5 + 9 = 14$
   $14 - \boxed{9} = 5$

3. Find the missing number.

   $64 + \boxed{36} = 100$

   $100 - 64 = \boxed{36}$

	6	tens	4	ones
	$\boxed{3}$	tens	$\boxed{6}$	ones
	9	tens	10	ones

Methods for Mental Addition

To add two numbers mentally, we can add the tens first and then add the ones.

1. What number is 56 more than 128?

   $128 + 56 = 184$

   $128 \xrightarrow{+50} 178 \xrightarrow{+6} 184$

   184 is 56 more than 128.

   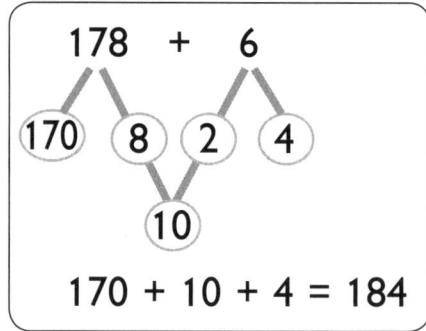

   $178 + 6$
   170 8 2 4
   10
   $170 + 10 + 4 = 184$

To add a number close to 100 mentally, we can make a 100 first and then add.

2. Add 367 and 98.

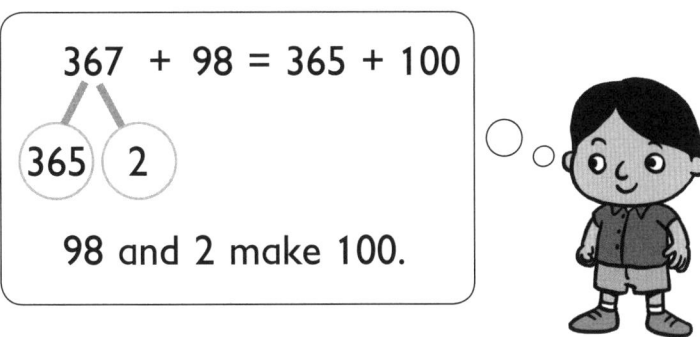

367 + 98 = 465

Methods for Mental Subtraction

To subtract mentally, we can subtract the tens and then subtract the ones.

1. Subtract 74 from 587.

   587 $\xrightarrow{-70}$ 517 $\xrightarrow{-4}$ 513

   587 − 74 = 513

2. Subtract 81 from 100.

   100 $\xrightarrow{-80}$ 20 $\xrightarrow{-1}$ 19

   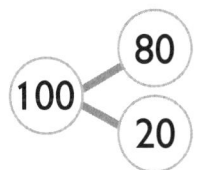

   100 − 81 = 19

To subtract a number close to 100 mentally, we can subtract from 100 first and then add.

2. Subtract 96 from 310.

$310 - 96 = 210 + 4$

210 100

Subtract 96 from 100.

$310 - 96 = 214$

Exercise 1 : Finding the Missing Number

1. Find the missing numbers.

    (a) ☐ − 50 = 26

    (b) 50 + ☐ = 76

    (c) ☐ + 15 = 60

    (d) ☐ − 45 = 15

2. Find the missing numbers.

    (a) ☐ − 25 = 25

    (b) 37 + 43 = ☐

    (c) ☐ − 55 = 40

    (d) 62 + 28 = ☐

    (e) 78 − ☐ = 48

    (f) 53 + ☐ = 90

    (g) 35 + ☐ = 100

3. Find the missing numbers.

   (a) ☐ − 50 = 600

   (b) 2 + ☐ = 750

   (c) 362 − ☐ = 100

   (d) ☐ + 3 = 360

4. Find the missing numbers.

   (a) 100 / 42, ☐

   (b) 100 / 78, ☐

   (c) 100 / ☐, 9

5. Find the missing numbers.

   (a) 57 + ☐ = 100

   (b) 35 + ☐ = 100

   (c) 100 − 17 = ☐

   (d) 100 − 82 = ☐

Exercise 2 : Methods for Mental Addition

1. Match.

626 + 98

525 + 70 + 5

747 + 54

747 + 50 + 4

525 + 75

624 + 100

819 + 92

811 + 100

425 + 97

363 + 99

422 + 100

362 + 100

2. Write the missing numbers.

(a) 45 + 25 = ☐

(b) 35 + 65 = ☐

(c) 15 + 35 = ☐

(d) 55 + 25 = ☐

(e) 99 + 5 = ☐

(f) 98 + 37 = ☐

(g) 315 + 71 = ☐

(h) 202 + 58 = ☐

(i) 578 + 27 = ☐

(j) 749 + 45 = ☐

(k) 834 + 97 = ☐

(l) 99 + 681 = ☐

Exercise 3 : Methods for Mental Subtraction

1. Match.

   436 − 96

   436 − 200 + 4

   436 − 98

   436 − 100 + 7

   436 − 196

   436 − 200 + 2

   436 − 93

   436 − 100 + 2

   436 − 198

   436 − 100 + 4

   436 − 193

   436 − 200 + 7

2. Write the missing numbers.

   (a) 60 − 35 = ☐

   (b) 90 − 75 = ☐

   (c) 80 − 15 = ☐

   (d) 85 − 45 = ☐

3. Subtract.

   (a) 100 − 54 = ☐

   (b) 100 − 44 = ☐

   (c) 100 − 65 = ☐

   (d) 100 − 82 = ☐

4. Subtract.

   (a) 100 − 40 = ☐   (b) 100 − 70 = ☐
       400 − 40 = ☐   400 − 70 = ☐
       600 − 40 = ☐   700 − 70 = ☐

   (c) 100 − 15 = ☐   (d) 100 − 65 = ☐
       300 − 15 = ☐   500 − 65 = ☐
       500 − 15 = ☐   800 − 65 = ☐

5. Write the missing numbers.

(a) 47 − 23 = ☐

(b) 95 − 62 = ☐

(c) 37 − 18 = ☐

(d) 81 − 46 = ☐

(e) 533 − 12 = ☐

(f) 367 − 57 = ☐

(g) 656 − 39 = ☐

(h) 124 − 78 = ☐

(i) 703 − 97 = ☐

(j) 506 − 98 = ☐

(k) 681 − 99 = ☐

(l) 952 − 98 = ☐

BLANK

Unit 7 : Multiplication and Division

Friendly Notes

Multiplying and Dividing by 4

We can count by 4's to help us remember the multiplication table of 4.

$1 \times 4 = 4$ $4 \div 4 = 1$	
$2 \times 4 = 8$ $8 \div 4 = 2$	
$3 \times 4 = 12$ $12 \div 4 = 3$	
$4 \times 4 = 16$ $16 \div 4 = 4$	
$5 \times 4 = 20$ $20 \div 4 = 5$	
$6 \times 4 = 24$ $24 \div 4 = 6$	
$7 \times 4 = 28$ $28 \div 4 = 7$	
$8 \times 4 = 32$ $32 \div 4 = 8$	
$9 \times 4 = 36$ $36 \div 4 = 9$	
$10 \times 4 = 40$ $40 \div 4 = 10$	

Multiplying and Dividing by 5

We can count by 5's to help us remember the multiplication table of 5.

$1 \times 5 = \mathbf{5}$ $5 \div 5 = 1$	
$2 \times 5 = \mathbf{10}$ $10 \div 5 = 2$	
$3 \times 5 = \mathbf{15}$ $15 \div 5 = 3$	
$4 \times 5 = \mathbf{20}$ $20 \div 5 = 4$	
$5 \times 5 = \mathbf{25}$ $25 \div 5 = 5$	
$6 \times 5 = \mathbf{30}$ $30 \div 5 = 6$	
$7 \times 5 = \mathbf{35}$ $35 \div 5 = 7$	
$8 \times 5 = \mathbf{40}$ $40 \div 5 = 8$	
$9 \times 5 = \mathbf{45}$ $45 \div 5 = 9$	
$10 \times 5 = \mathbf{50}$ $50 \div 5 = 10$	

Multiplying and Dividing by 10

We can count by 10's to help us remember the multiplication table of 10.

1 × 10 = **10** 10 ÷ 10 = 1	
2 × 10 = **20** 20 ÷ 10 = 2	
3 × 10 = **30** 30 ÷ 10 = 3	
4 × 10 = **40** 40 ÷ 10 = 4	
5 × 10 = **50** 50 ÷ 10 = 5	
6 × 10 = **60** 60 ÷ 10 = 6	
7 × 10 = **70** 70 ÷ 10 = 7	
8 × 10 = **80** 80 ÷ 10 = 8	
9 × 10 = **90** 90 ÷ 10 = 9	
10 × 10 = **100** 100 ÷ 10 = 10	

BLANK

Exercise 1 : Multiplying and Dividing by 4

1. Fill in the boxes.

   (a) $3 \times 4 = \boxed{}$

   $4 \times 3 = \boxed{}$

   (b) $4 \times 5 = \boxed{}$

   $5 \times 4 = \boxed{}$

   (c) $6 \times 4 = \boxed{}$

   $4 \times 6 = \boxed{}$

   $9 \times 4 = \boxed{}$

   $4 \times 9 = \boxed{}$

2. Fill in the boxes.

   (a) Multiply 3 by 4. $3 \times 4 = \boxed{}$

   (b) Multiply 6 by 4. $6 \times 4 = \boxed{}$

   (c) Multiply 9 by 4. $9 \times 4 = \boxed{}$

   (d) Multiply 8 by 4. $8 \times 4 = \boxed{}$

3. Fill in the boxes.

(a) 4 × 4 is 4 more than 3 × 4.   3 × 4 = 12
                                    4 × 4 = ☐

(b) 6 × 4 is 4 more than 5 × 4.   5 × 4 = 20
                                    6 × 4 = ☐

(c) 7 × 4 is 4 less than 8 × 4.   8 × 4 = 32
                                    7 × 4 = ☐

(d) 9 × 4 is 4 less than 10 × 4.   10 × 4 = 40
                                    9 × 4 = ☐

4. Write the missing numbers.

(a) 24 ÷ 4 = ☐   (b) 20 ÷ 4 = ☐
(c) 36 ÷ 4 = ☐   (d) 40 ÷ 4 = ☐

5. Write the missing numbers.

(a) 3 × 4 = 12   (b) 8 × 4 = 32
    12 ÷ 4 = ☐   32 ÷ 4 = ☐

(c) ☐ × 4 = 28   (d) ☐ × 4 = 36
    28 ÷ 4 = ☐   36 ÷ 4 = ☐

(e) 5 × 4 = ☐   (f) 10 × 4 = ☐
    ☐ ÷ 4 = 5   40 ÷ 4 = ☐

6. Solve.
   (a) Lindsey bought 4 books.
       Each book cost $6.
       How much did she pay for the books?

   (b) Cameron put 34 fish equally in 4 tanks.
       How many fish were there in each tank?
       How many fish were not in the tank?

   (c) There are 10 tennis balls in each box.
       How many tennis balls are there in 4 such boxes?

(d) There are 28 pages in a storybook.
Mervyn reads 4 pages every day.
How long does Mervyn take to read the storybook?

(e) Ruth has 4 strings.
She put 5 beads on each string.
How many beads are there altogether?

(f) There are 4 monkeys in a zoo.
Each monkey eats 5 bananas in the morning and 4 bananas in the afternoon.
How many bananas do they eat every day?

Exercise 2 : Multiplying and Dividing by 5

1. Fill in the boxes.

    (a) Multiply 5 by 5. 5×5 = ☐

    (b) Multiply 8 by 5. 8×5 = ☐

    (c) Multiply 7 by 5. 7×5 = ☐

    (d) Multiply 10 by 5. 10×5 = ☐

2. Write the missing numbers.

    (a) 4×5 = ☐   (b) 5×3 = ☐

    (c) $10 \div 5$ = ☐   (d) $40 \div 5$ = ☐

    (e) $25 \div 5$ = ☐   (f) $20 \div 5$ = ☐

3. Write the missing numbers.

    (a) 2×5 = ☐   (b) 7×5 = ☐
       $10 \div 5$ = ☐ $35 \div 5$ = ☐

    (c) ☐ $\times 5 = 45$ (d) ☐ $\times 5 = 30$
       $45 \div 5$ = ☐ $30 \div 5$ = ☐

4. Solve.
    (a) Ethan drinks 6 glasses of water every day. How many glasses of water will he drink in 5 days?

    (b) Sheena does 5 pages of math practice every week. How many weeks will she take to finish 48 pages? How many pages does she have left?

    (c) Mrs. Tweed paid $35 for 5 yd of cloth. What was the cost of 1 yd of cloth?

Exercise 3 : Multiplying and Dividing by 10

1. Multiply or divide.

    (a) 10 × 4 = ☐   (b) 10 × 6 = ☐

    (c) 10 × 8 = ☐   (d) 10 × 10 = ☐

    (e) 20 ÷ 10 = ☐   (f) 10 ÷ 10 = ☐

    (g) 40 ÷ 10 = ☐   (h) 90 ÷ 10 = ☐

2. Write the missing numbers.

    (a) 3 × 10 = ☐   (b) 7 × 10 = ☐

        30 ÷ 10 = ☐   70 ÷ 10 = ☐

3. Solve.

    (a) Mr. Cohen gave $50 to 10 children to share equally.
    How much did each child get?

(b) John saves $10 each month.
How much will he save in 10 months?

(c) Tolga paid $80 for 10 water bottles.
What was the cost of 1 water bottle?

(d) Mr. Falkan sold 8 sets of storybooks yesterday.
There were 10 books in each set.
How many storybooks did Mr. Falkan sell?

Unit 8 : Money

Friendly Notes

Dollars and Cents

When we write money in dollars and cents, the dot (.) separates the cents from the dollars.

We write 6 dollars 10 cents as $6.10.

Write the prices of these items in dollars and cents.

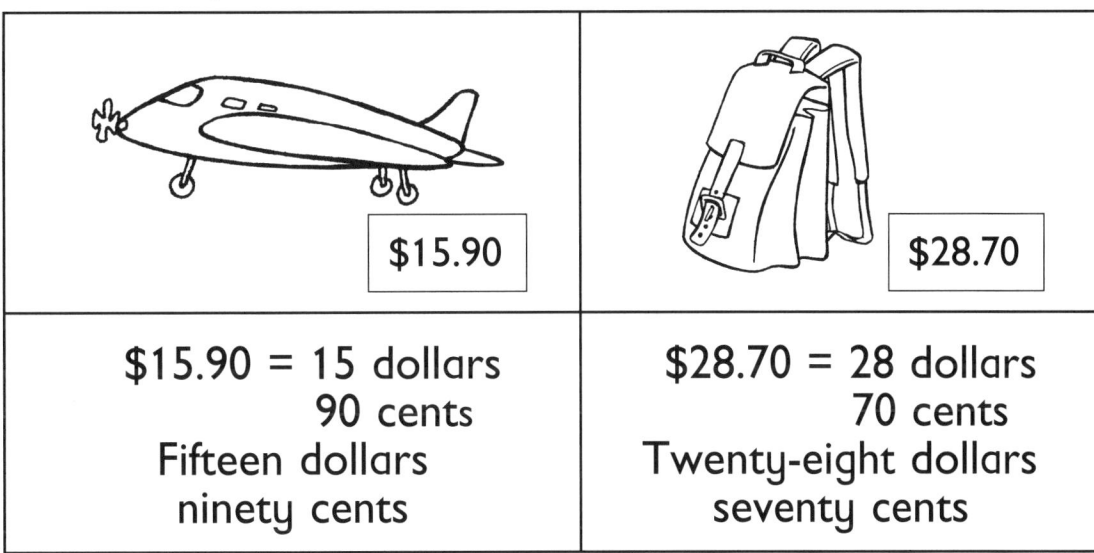

Adding Money

When we add money, we add the dollars together and add the cents together.

1. $9.30 + $6.45 = $ _____

    Add the dollars : $9 + $6 = $15
    Add the cents   : 30¢ + 45¢ = 75¢

    Total: $9.30 + $6.45 = $15 + 75¢
                        = $15.75

    We can also add $9.30 and $6.45 in this way:

    $9.30 $\xrightarrow{+\$6}$ $15.30 $\xrightarrow{+45¢}$ $15.75

2. $8.25 + $1.35 = $ _____

    We can add $8.25 and $1.35 like this:

    $ 8 . 2 5
    + $ 1 . 3 5
    ―――――――――
    $ 9 . 6 0

    $\overset{1}{8}\ 2\ 5$
    + 1 3 5
    ―――――――
    9 6 0

Subtracting Money

When there are not enough cents to take away from, change $1 into 100 cents.

1. $6.55 − $2.30 = $ _____

    $6.55 $\xrightarrow{-\$2}$ $4.55 $\xrightarrow{-30¢}$ $4.25

    $6.55 − $2.30 = $4.25

2. $7.30 − $4.65 = $ _____

    We cannot take away 65 cents from 30 cents.
    We change $1 into 100 cents.

    $7.30 = $6 + 130¢
    Subtract the dollars: $6 − $4 = $2
    Subtract the cents: 130¢ − 65¢ = 65¢
    $7.30 − $4.65 = $2.65

3. $4.85 − $2.95 = $ _____
   We can subtract $2.95 from $4.85 like this:

   ```
    $ 4 . 8 5
   − $ 2 . 9 5
   ─────────
    $ 1 . 9 0
   ```

   ```
       3 18
       4̷ 8̷ 5
   −   2  9 5
   ─────────
       1  9 0
   ```

4. Jackson bought a wallet for $16.35.
   He also bought a pair of shorts.
   The pair of shorts cost $5.50 less than the wallet.
   (a) How much did Jackson pay for the pair of shorts?
   (b) How much did he spend altogether?

   (a)
   $16.35 = $15 + 135¢
   $15 − $5 = $10
   135¢ − 50¢ = 85¢

   $16.35 − $5.50 = $10.85

   Jackson paid $10.85 for the pair of shorts.

   (b) $16.35 —+$10→ $26.35 —+85¢→ $27.20

   35¢ + 85¢ = 120¢
   120¢ = $1 + 20¢

   $16.35 + $10.85 = $27.20
   He spent $27.20 altogether.

Exercise 1 : Dollars and Cents

1. Write the correct amount of money.

   (a)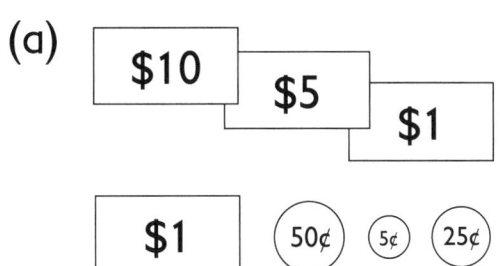

   $ _____

   (b)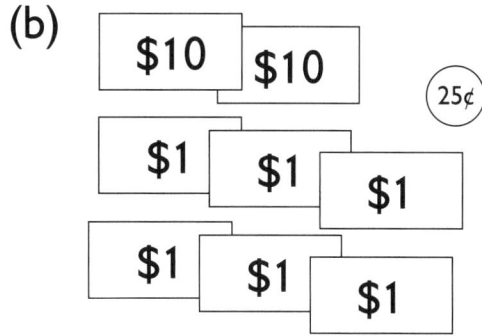

   $ _____

   (c)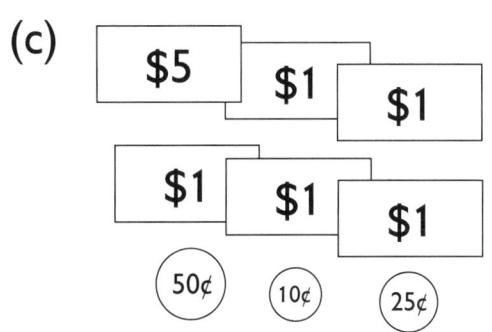

   $ _____

   (d)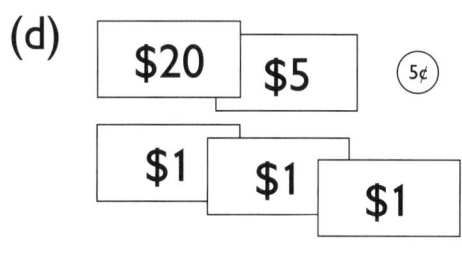

   $ _____

   (e)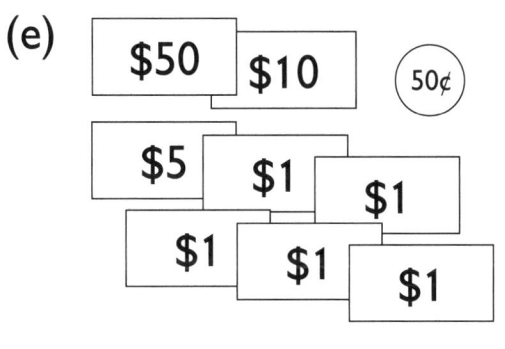

   $ _____

   (f)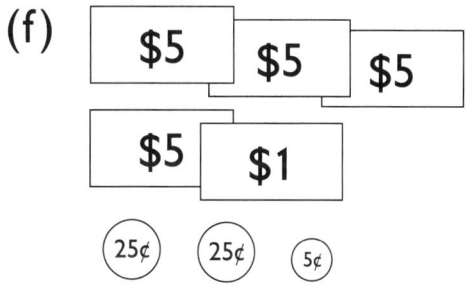

   $ _____

2. Write the missing numbers.

   (a) $0.75 = _____ dollars _____ cents

   (b) $7.35 = _____ dollars _____ cents

   (c) $12.05 = _____ dollars _____ cents

   (d) $48.10 = _____ dollars _____ cents

   (e) $77.15 = _____ dollars _____ cents

3. Write in dollars.

   (a) 95 cents = $_____

   (b) 6 dollars 5 cents = $_____

   (c) 18 dollars 60 cents = $_____

   (d) 20 dollars 55 cents = $_____

   (e) 39 dollars 90 cents = $_____

4. Complete the table.

(a)	Fifty cents	$
(b)	Fourteen dollars thirty cents	$
(c)		$15.25
(d)		$40.45
(e)	Seventy-one dollars eighty-five cents	
(f)		$98.05

5. Write in dollars.
   (a) 125¢ = $_____
   (b) 605¢ = $_____
   (c) 7¢ = $_____
   (d) 60¢ = $_____
   (e) 235¢ = $_____
   (f) 500¢ = $_____

6. Write in cents.
   (a) $0.95 = _____¢
   (b) $1.65 = _____¢
   (c) $2.83 = _____¢
   (d) $7.90 = _____¢
   (e) $0.05 = _____¢
   (f) $5.00 = _____¢

7. Fill in the blanks.
   (a) 5 fifty-cent coins = $_____
   (b) 4 quarters = $_____
   (c) 6 dimes = $_____

8. Fill in the boxes.

　　Example:
　　| 13 | dimes = $1.30

　　(a) [　　] one-dollar bills = $28.00

　　(b) [　　] half-dollars = $5.50

　　(c) [　　] quarters = $1.50

　　(d) [　　] nickels = $0.95

　　(e) [　　] dimes = $10.00

　　(f) [　　] fifty-cent coins = $30.00

Exercise 2 : Adding Money

1. Write the missing numbers.

   (a) 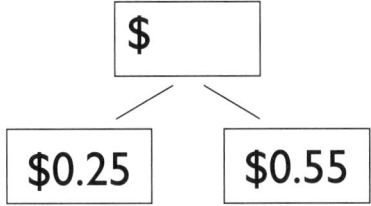   (b)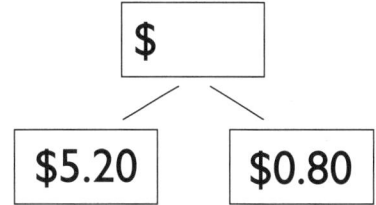

   (c) 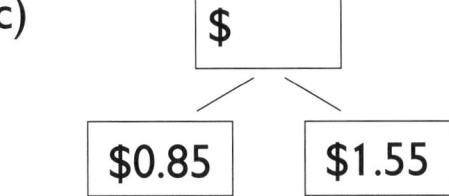   (d)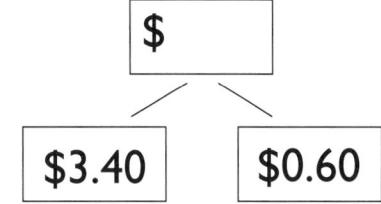

2. Write the missing numbers.

   (a) 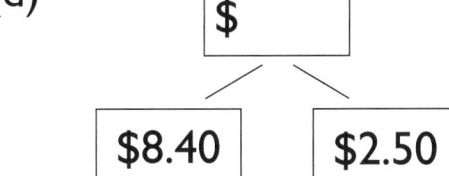   (b)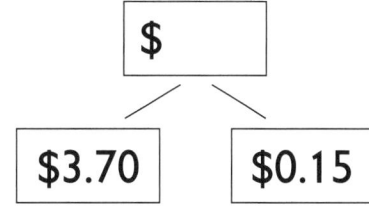

   (c) 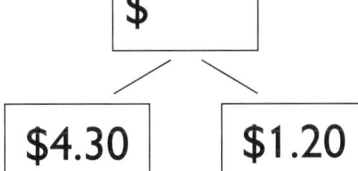   (d)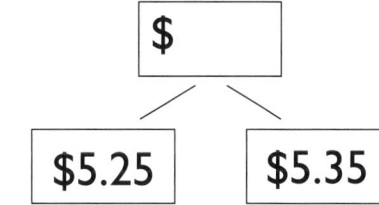

3. Write the missing numbers.

(a) 43¢ + 39¢ = _____ ¢

(b) 25¢ + 68¢ = _____ ¢

(c) $4.65 + 25¢ = $_____

(d) $9.05 + 70¢ = $_____

(e) $8.25 + $0.55 = $_____

(f) $4.99 + $2.25 = $_____

(g) $5.85 + $3.80 = $_____

(h) $7.60 + $9.50 = $_____

4. Add.

(a) $ 1.68
  + $ 0.56
  _____

(b) $ 1.36
  + $ 2.65
  _____

(c) $ 2.49
  + $ 0.98
  _____

(d) $ 3.08
  + $ 4.92
  _____

(e) $ 5.36
  + $ 3.17
  _____

(f) $ 3.25
  + $ 2.77
  _____

5. Solve.
   (a) Ryan saved $80.
       He saved $35 less than Lisa.
       How much did Lisa save?

   (b) After buying this set of books, Jane had $5 left.
       How much money did she have at first?

(c) A doll costs $9.65.
A toy airplane costs $12 more than the doll.
How much does the toy airplane cost?

(d) Mr. Mandela bought vegetables for $12.50.
He spent $15.60 more on fish.
How much did he spend on fish?

Exercise 3 : Subtracting Money

1. Write the missing numbers.

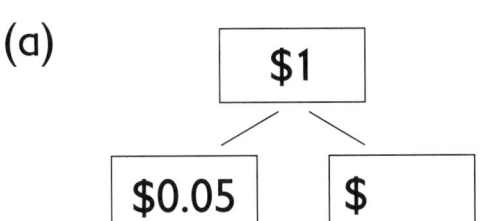
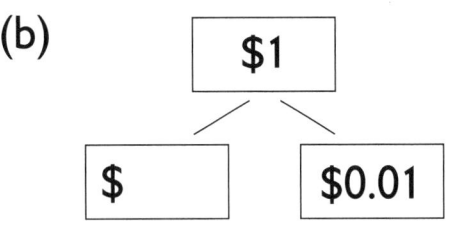

2. Write the missing numbers.

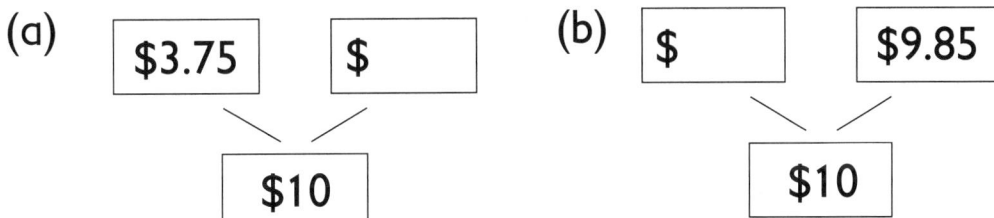

3. Write the missing numbers.

(a) 43¢ – 30¢ = _____ ¢

(b) 80¢ – 68¢ = _____ ¢

(c) $5 – 80¢ = $_____

(d) $9 – 15¢ = $_____

(e) $4.60 – 85¢ = $_____

(f) $9.00 – $6.85 = $_____

4. Solve.
   (a) Mr. Chen bought a watermelon for $2.65.
       He gave the shopkeeper $10.
       How much change did he get?

   (b) Nicole has $9.95.
       She wants to buy a dress that costs $25.70.
       How much more money does she need?

   (c) Raman had $60.65.
       He spent $38.95 on a watch.
       How much money did he have left?

Unit 9 : Fractions

Friendly Notes

Halves, Fourths, and Thirds

When we divide a whole into 2 equal parts, each part is one-half.
When we divide a whole into 4 equal parts, each part is one-quarter.
One-quarter is the same as one-fourth.
When we divide a whole into 3 equal parts, each part is one-third.

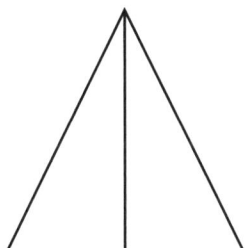

The triangle is divided into 2 equal parts.
Each part is a half.
2 halves make 1 whole.

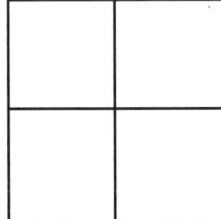

The square is divided into 4 equal parts.
Each part is a fourth.
4 fourths make 1 whole.

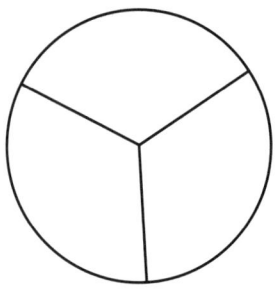

The circle is divided into 3 equal parts.
Each part is a third.
3 thirds make 1 whole.

Writing Fractions

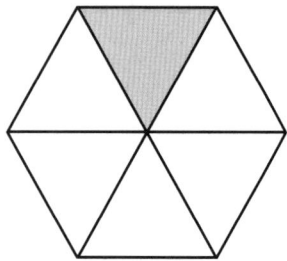

1 out of 6 equal parts is shaded.

$\frac{1}{6}$ of the shape is shaded.

5 out of 6 equal parts is not shaded.

$\frac{5}{6}$ of the shape is not shaded.

$\frac{1}{6}$ and $\frac{5}{6}$ make one whole.

We can use number lines to show fractions.

0 to 1 on a number line represents 1 whole.

The number line is divided into four equal parts. Each part is $\frac{1}{4}$.

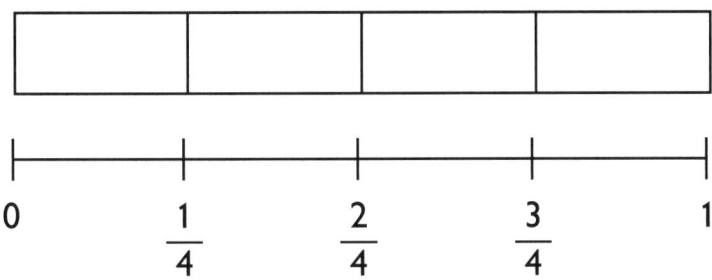

The fraction of each equal part of a whole gets smaller as the number of equal parts in a whole increases.

1. Which is greater, $\frac{1}{2}$ or $\frac{1}{8}$?

   Compare the size of the shaded parts.

   $\frac{1}{2}$ is greater.

2. Arrange the fractions in order.
   Begin with the greatest.

   $\frac{1}{9}$, $\frac{1}{6}$, $\frac{1}{10}$

   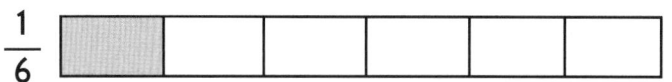

   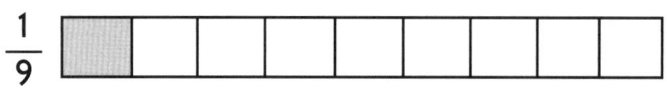

   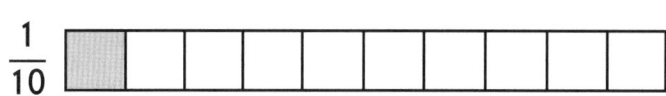

   Compare the size of the shaded parts.

   $\frac{1}{6}$ is the greatest.

   $\frac{1}{10}$ is the smallest.

   Arranging the fractions in order beginning with the greatest, we have $\frac{1}{6}$, $\frac{1}{9}$, $\frac{1}{10}$.

Exercise 1 : Halves, Fourths, and Thirds

1. Write **Yes** or **No** in the boxes.

    (a)

    The cake is cut into halves.

    (b)

    The shaded part shows one half of the shape.

2. Check (✓) the boxes for the shapes that show $\frac{1}{2}$ shaded.

   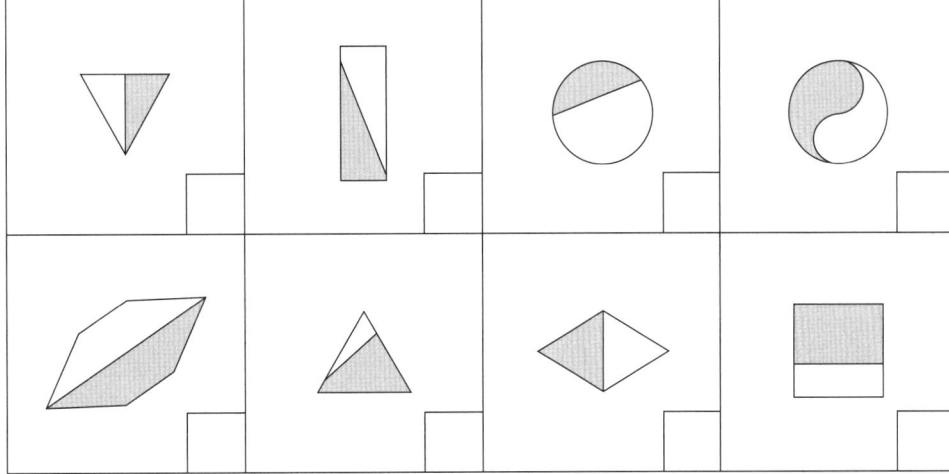

3. Check (✓) the boxes for the shapes that show $\frac{1}{4}$ shaded.

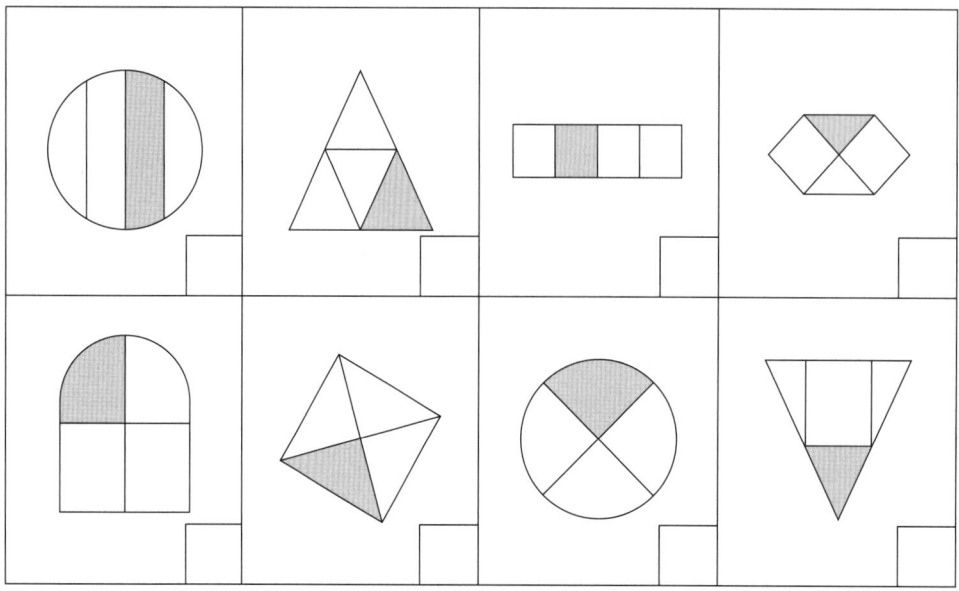

4. Check (✓) the boxes for the shapes that show $\frac{1}{3}$ shaded.

Exercise 2 : Writing Fractions

1. Match.

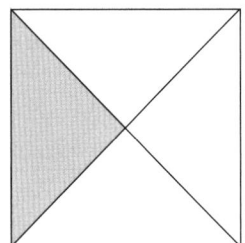 •   • $\dfrac{5}{6}$

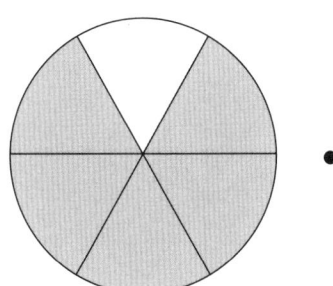 •   • $\dfrac{1}{4}$

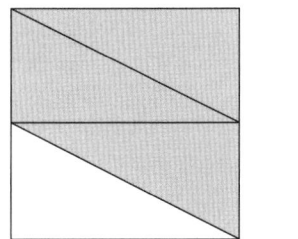 •   • $\dfrac{1}{2}$

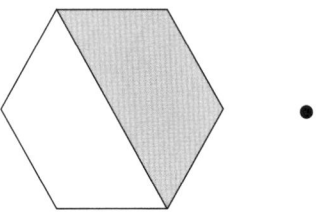 •   • $\dfrac{2}{3}$

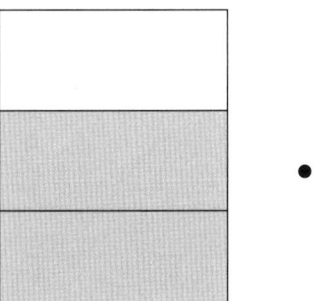 •   • $\dfrac{3}{4}$

2. What fraction of each shape is shaded?

(a)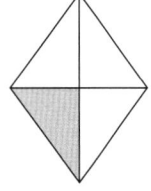

(b)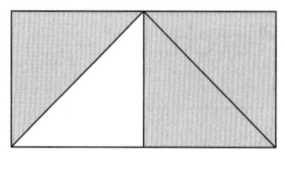

(c)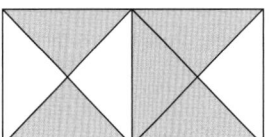

(d)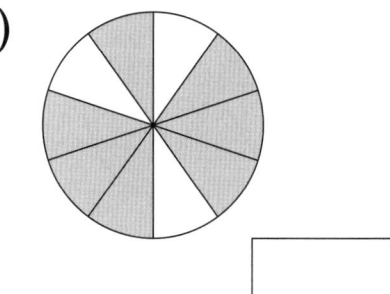

(e)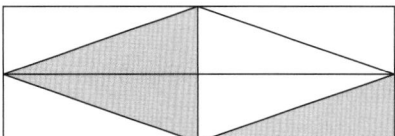

(f)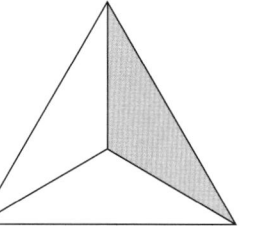

3. Fill in the blanks.

   (a) 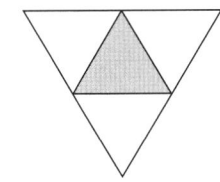 The triangle is divided into 4 equal parts.

   _____ out of the _____ equal parts is shaded.

   _____ of the triangle is shaded.

   (b) 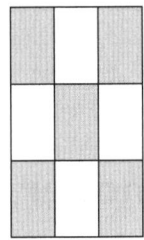 The rectangle is divided into 9 equal parts.

   _____ out of the _____ equal parts are shaded.

   _____ of the rectangle is shaded.

   (c) 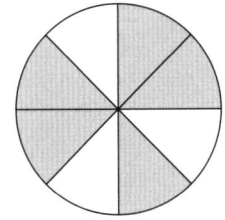 The circle is divided into 8 equal parts.

   _____ out of the _____ equal parts are shaded.

   _____ of the circle is shaded.

4. Use the fraction bars below to complete the following.

[Fraction bars showing $\frac{1}{2}$, $\frac{1}{3}$, $\frac{1}{4}$, $\frac{1}{5}$, $\frac{1}{6}$, $\frac{1}{8}$, $\frac{1}{10}$]

Fill in the blanks with **greater** or **smaller**.

(a) $\frac{1}{2}$ is _____ than $\frac{1}{4}$.

(b) $\frac{1}{4}$ is _____ than $\frac{1}{3}$.

(c) $\frac{1}{8}$ is _____ than $\frac{1}{6}$.

(d) $\frac{1}{5}$ is _____ than $\frac{1}{10}$.

(e) $\frac{1}{10}$ is _____ than $\frac{1}{4}$.

5. Circle the greater fraction.

   (a) $\dfrac{1}{4}$, $\dfrac{3}{4}$ (b) $\dfrac{4}{5}$, $\dfrac{2}{5}$

6. Circle the smaller fraction.

   (a) $\dfrac{4}{5}$, $\dfrac{5}{5}$ (b) $\dfrac{5}{8}$, $\dfrac{3}{8}$

7. Circle the greatest fraction.

   (a) $\dfrac{1}{4}$, $\dfrac{1}{3}$, $\dfrac{1}{5}$ (b) $\dfrac{1}{5}$, $\dfrac{1}{10}$, $\dfrac{1}{6}$

8. Circle the smallest fraction.

   (a) $\dfrac{1}{4}$, $\dfrac{1}{6}$, $\dfrac{1}{8}$ (b) $\dfrac{1}{10}$, $\dfrac{1}{8}$, $\dfrac{1}{5}$

9. Arrange the fractions in order.
   Begin with the smallest.

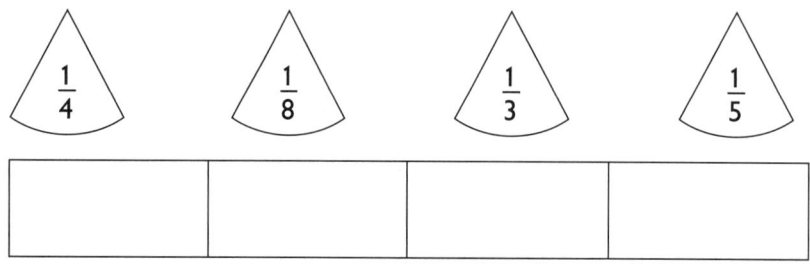

   smallest

10. Arrange the fractions in order.
    Begin with the greatest.

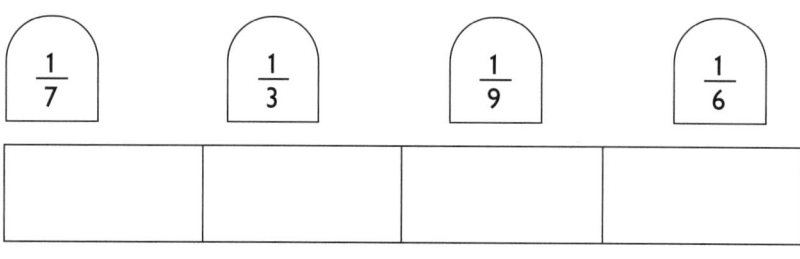

    greatest

11. Fill in the boxes.

    (a) $\frac{2}{3}$ and ☐ make 1 whole.

    (b) $\frac{3}{8}$ and ☐ make 1 whole.

12. Write the missing fractions.

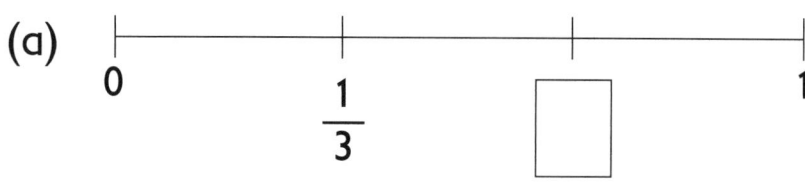

Unit 10 : Time

Friendly Notes

Telling Time After the Hour

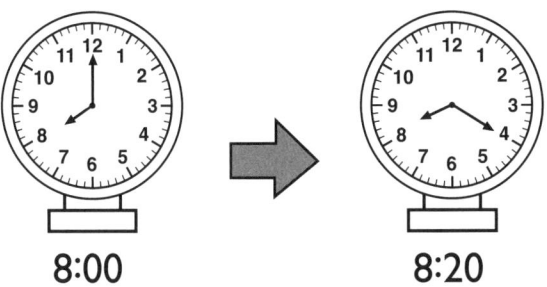

8:00   8:20

We read 8:20 as eight twenty.
It is 20 minutes **after** 8 o'clock.
We can also say it is 20 minutes **past** 8.

Telling Time Before the Hour

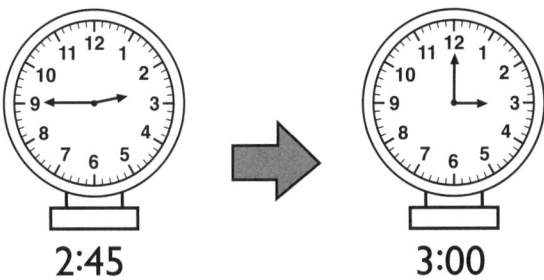

2:45   3:00

We read 2:45 as two forty-five.
It is 15 minutes **before** 3 o'clock.
We can also say it is 15 minutes **to** 3.

We use A.M. to indicate time before 12 noon.
We use P.M. to indicate time after 12 noon.

It is morning.
Maria wakes up at 6:30 A.M.

It is noon.
Ricky has lunch at 12 P.M.

It is evening.
Jacob has piano lessons at 7:45 P.M.

It is night.
Tricia goes to bed at 9:15 P.M.

Exercise 1 : Telling Time After the Hour

1. Fill in the blanks.

    (a)

    9 o'clock   _____ minutes
                       after 9 o'clock

    (b)

    3 o'clock   _____ minutes
                       after 3 o'clock

    (c)

    8 o'clock   _____ minutes
                       after 8 o'clock

2. Fill in the blanks.

(a)
___ minutes past 4

(b)
___ minutes past 2

(c)
___ minutes past 12

(d)
___ minutes past 8

(e)
___ minutes past 7

(f)
___ minutes past 6

(g)
___ minutes past 1

(h)
___ minutes past 3

Name: _____ Class: _____ Date: _____

Exercise 2 : Telling Time Before the Hour

1. Fill in the blanks.

   (a)    _____ minutes before _____ o'clock.

   _____ minutes to _____ o'clock.

   (b)    _____ minutes before _____ o'clock.

   _____ minutes to _____ o'clock.

   (c)    _____ minutes before _____ o'clock.

   _____ minutes to _____ o'clock.

   (d)    _____ minutes before _____ o'clock.

   _____ minutes to _____ o'clock.

2. Fill in the blanks.

   (a) 8:55

   _____ minutes to _____

   (b) 1:45

   _____ minutes to _____

   (c) 7:35

   _____ minutes to _____

3. Fill in the blanks with A.M. or P.M.

   (a) Craig goes to school everyday at 8:00 _____ in the morning.

   (b) Gwen had supper at 10:50 _____ at night.

   (c) Rosie had a tennis match at 9:45 _____ in the morning.

   (d) Mr. Farell watched a movie in the evening at 6:55 _____.

Unit 11 : Tables and Graphs

Friendly Notes

Picture Graphs, Bar Graphs, and Line Plots

We can present data using picture graphs, bar graphs, or line plots.
Pictures are used to show data in picture graphs.
Bars are used to show data in bar graphs.

Count each type of flower shown.

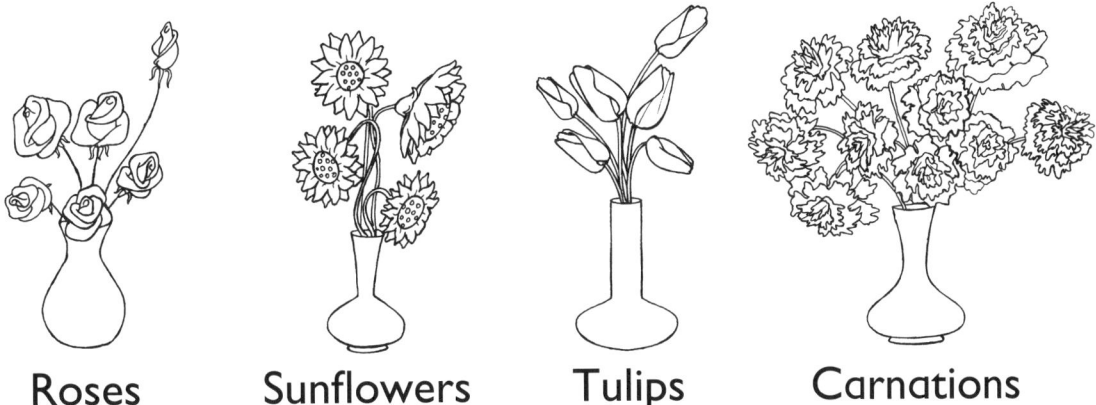

Roses   Sunflowers   Tulips   Carnations

We can tally as we count, and write the tally marks in a chart.

Flower	
Rose	//// /
Sunflower	////
Tulip	//// /
Carnation	//// ////

The picture graph below shows the number of each type of flower.

Rose	Sunflower	Tulip	Carnation

Each 🌸 stands for 2 flowers.

From the graph we can get the following information.

(a) Each 🌸 stands for 2 flowers.

(b) There are 6 roses.

(c) There are 4 sunflowers.

(d) There are 6 tulips.

(e) There are 10 carnations.

(f) There are 2 fewer sunflowers than roses.

(g) There are 4 more carnations than tulips.

(h) There are as many roses as tulips.

(i) There are 26 flowers altogether.

The bar graphs below show the number of each type of flower.

(a) Vertical bar graph

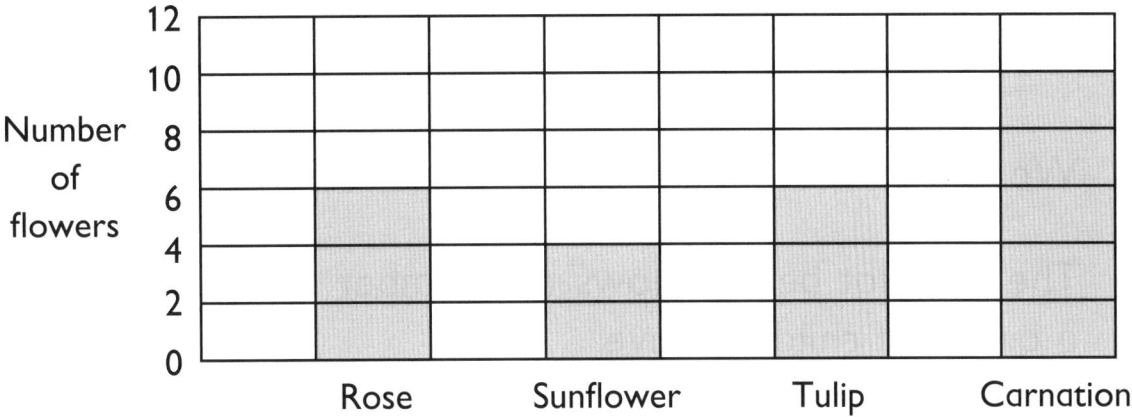

(b) Horizontal bar graph

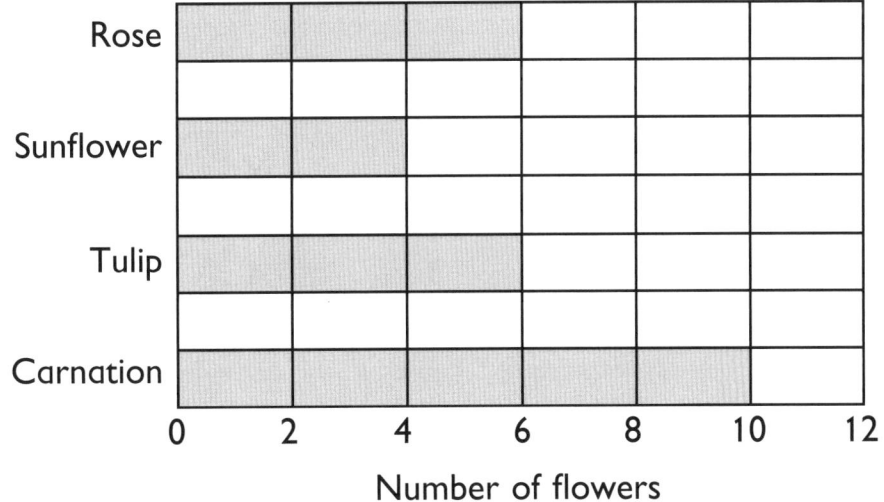

The table below shows the number of each type of flower.

Flower	Rose	Sunflower	Tulip	Carnation
Number of flowers	6	4	6	10

We can also use a line plot to record data.

The line plot below shows the number of siblings a group of children have.

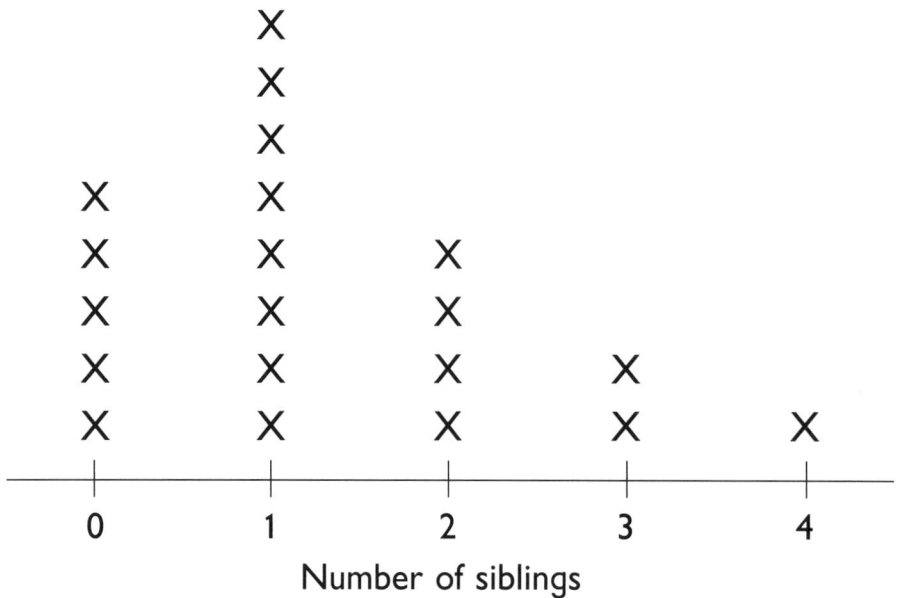

Number of siblings

From the line plot, we can get the following information.

(a) Most children have 1 sibling.

(b) The least number of children have 4 siblings.

(c) There are a total of 20 children in the survey.

Exercise 1 : Picture Graphs

1. Fill in the blanks.

    (a) Each ○ stands for 5 oranges.

    ○○○○○○○ stand for _____ oranges.

    (b) Each ▲ stands for 10 trees.

    ▲▲▲▲▲▲▲▲ stand for _____ trees.

    (c) Each □ stands for 4 television sets.

    □□□□□□ stand for _____ television sets.

    (d) Each ♀ stands for 3 balloons.

    ♀♀♀♀♀♀♀ stand for _____ balloons.

    (e) Each △ stands for 4 houses.
    Color the correct number of triangles to show 32 houses.

    △ △ △ △ △ △ △ △ △ △

2. The picture graph below shows the number of students who like each type of sports.

Swimming	😊 😊 😊 😊 😊
Badminton	😊 😊 😊
Football	😊 😊 😊 😊 😊 😊
Basketball	😊 😊

Each 😊 stands for 2 students.

Use the graph to complete the following.

(a) _____ students like football.

(b) _____ students like swimming.

(c) _____ is the most popular sport.

(d) _____ more students like swimming than basketball.

(e) _____ fewer students like badminton than football.

3. The picture graph below shows the number of books read by 5 children.

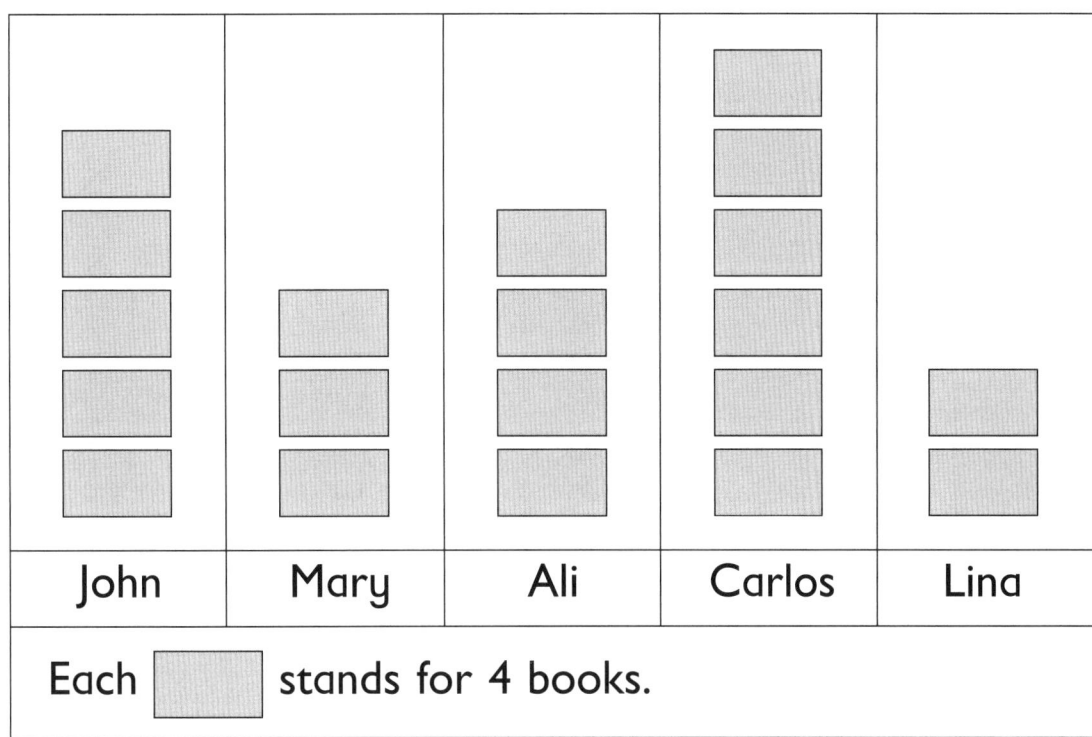

Use the graph to complete the following.

(a) Carlos read _____ books.

(b) Mary and Ali read _____ books altogether.

(c) John read _____ more books than Lina.

(d) Ali read _____ fewer books than Carlos.

(e) If Lina took 5 days to read each book, she took _____ days to read all her books.

4. The picture graph shows the number of each animal in a zoo.

Use the graph to complete the following.

(a) There are _____ penguins.

(b) There are _____ monkeys.

(c) There are _____ fewer deers than bears.

(d) There are _____ more bears than penguins.

(e) The total number of _____ and _____ is the same as the total number of bears.

Exercise 2 : Bar Graphs

1. The bar graph below shows the number of students who like math, English, science, and music.

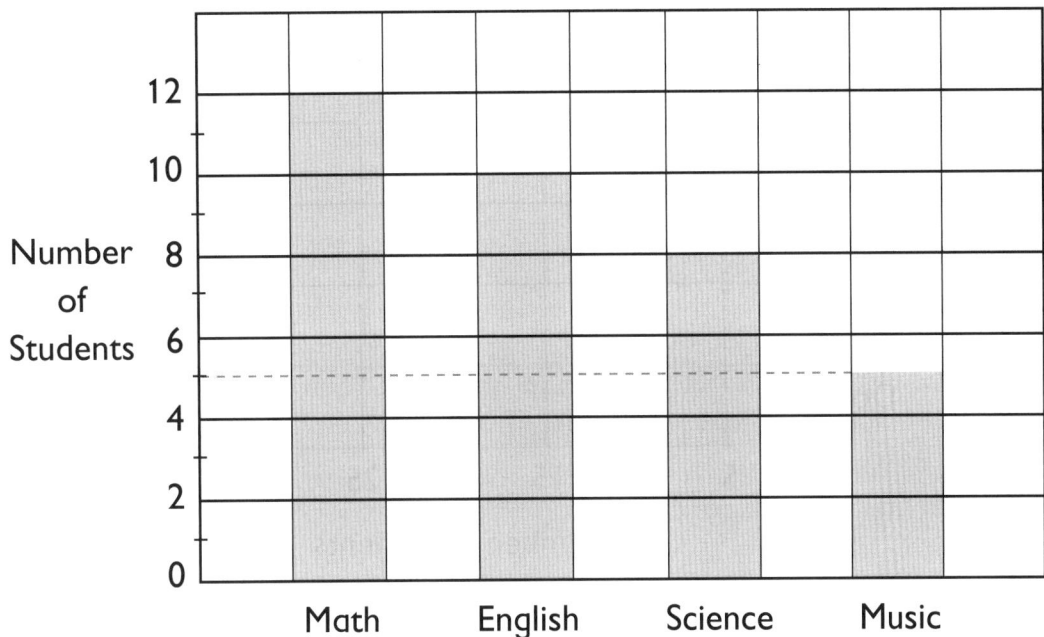

Use the graph to answer the following questions.

(a) How many students like math?

_____

(b) How many students like English? _____

(c) How many students like science? _____

(d) How many more students like math than science? _____

(e) How many fewer students like music than English? _____

2. The bar graph below shows the number of students who have each type of pet.

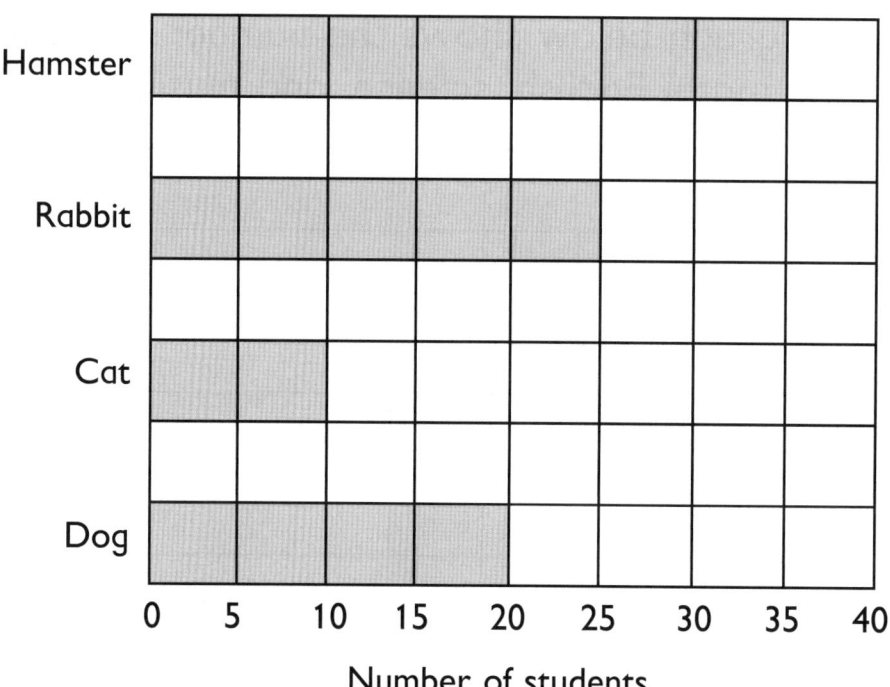

Use the graph to answer the following questions.

(a) How many students have dogs as pets?
_____

(b) What is the total number of students who have rabbits and hamsters as pets?
_____

(c) How many more students have rabbits as pets than cats? _____

(d) How many fewer students have dogs as pets than hamsters? _____

Exercise 3 : Line Plots

1. The table below shows the number of children from each Grade 1 class that took part in a drawing competition.

Class	1A	1B	1C	1D	1E	1F	1G
Number of children	5	11	9	16	12	8	15

Complete the following line plot with the data given in the table. Then answer the following questions.

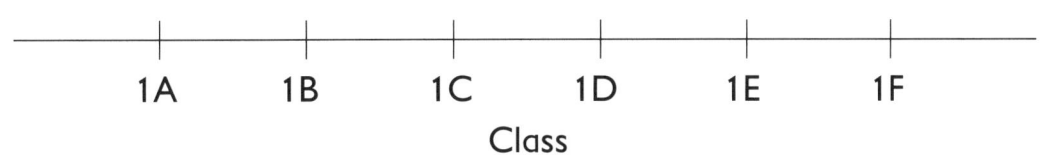

(a) How many children from Grade 1 took part in the competition? _____

(b) The greatest number of participants came from Class _____.

(c) For the grade to get free crayon sets, each grade must have 100 participants.
How many more participants are required from Grade 1? _____

2. The line plot below shows the amount of money saved by students in a month in Class 2A.

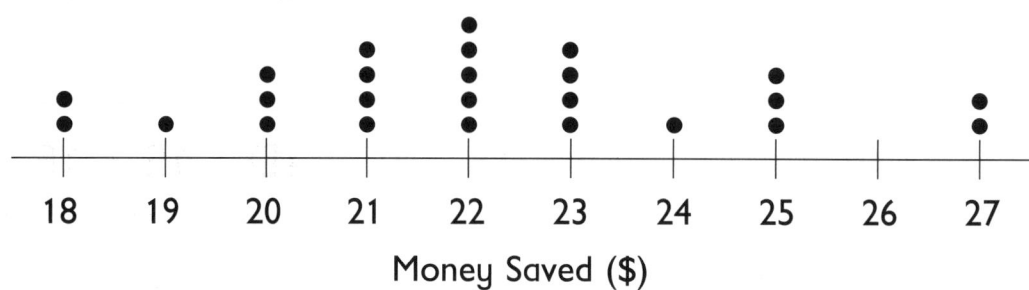

Use the line plot to answer the following questions.

(a) How many students were surveyed? _____

(b) What is the most common amount saved?
$_____

(c) Suggest a reason why most students in the class saved this amount.

_____

_____

Unit 12 : Geometry

Friendly Notes

Flat and Curved Surfaces

Objects come in different shapes and sizes.
They can have flat or curved surfaces.

Objects with flat surfaces	Objects with curved surfaces	Objects with flat and curved surfaces

These objects have flat and curved faces too.

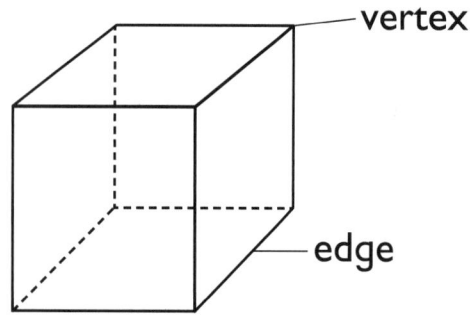

This solid has 6 flat faces, 8 vertices, and 12 edges.

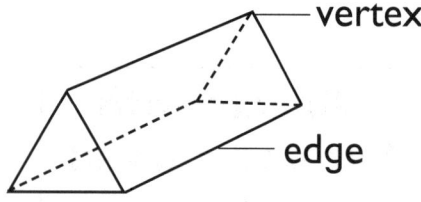

This solid has 5 flat faces, 6 vertices, and 9 edges.

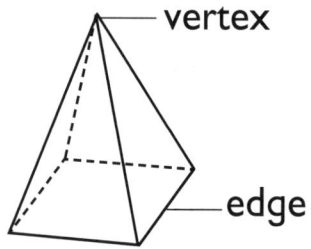

This solid has 5 flat faces, 5 vertices, and 8 edges.

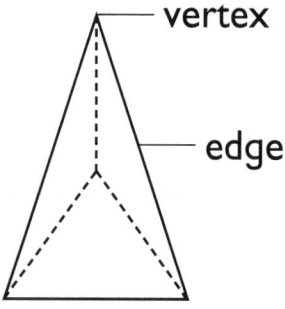

This solid has 4 flat faces, 4 vertices, and 6 edges.

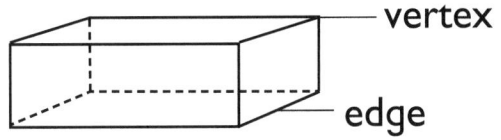 This solid has 6 flat faces, 8 vertices, and 12 edges.

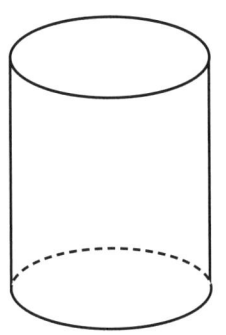 This solid has 1 curved face and 2 flat faces.

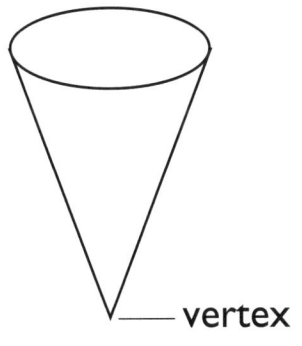 This solid has 1 flat face, 1 curved face, and 1 vertex.

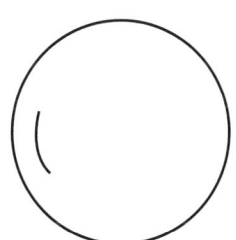 This solid has 1 curved face. It has no vertices and no edges.

Composite Figures

We can put shapes such as squares, triangles, rectangles, and circles together to form other shapes.

We can make the shape below with a triangle and a half circle.
The shape is made up of 3 straight lines and a curve.

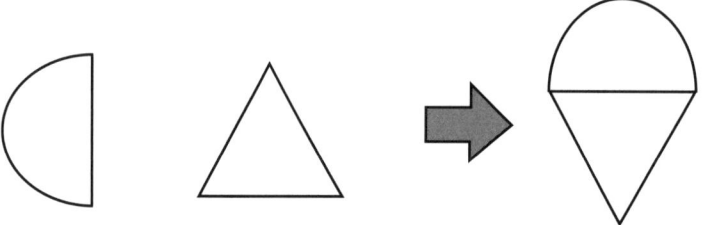

We can make the shape below using 2 triangles, 2 rectangles, and a square.

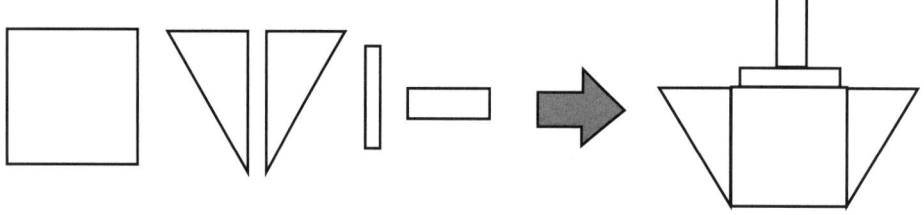

This is a regular pattern of shapes.
What shape comes next?

The next shape is □.

Some squares are fitted together to form a rectangle.

This rectangle is made up of 20 squares.

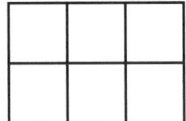

This rectangle is made up of 6 squares.

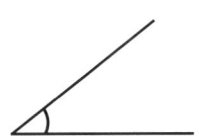

Angles and Shapes

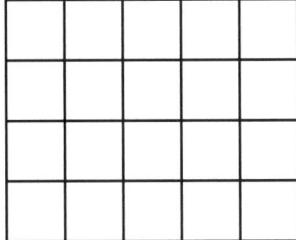 Any two sides joined makes an angle.

△	A triangle has 3 sides and 3 angles.
▱	A quadrilateral has 4 sides and 4 angles.
⬠	A pentagon has 5 sides and 5 angles.

A polygon is a closed figure with straight sides.

	A hexagon has 6 sides and 6 angles.
	An octagon has 8 sides and 8 angles.

Exercise 1 : Flat and Curved Surfaces

1. Name the shape of the face which is shaded.

   (a)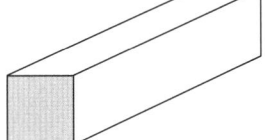

   (b)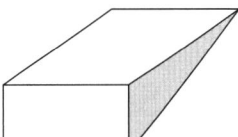

   _____   _____

   (c)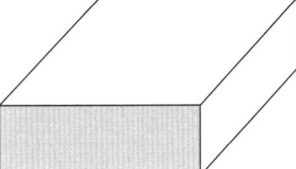

   (d)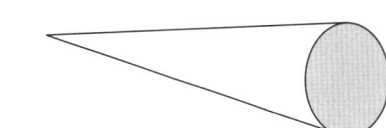

   _____   _____

   (e)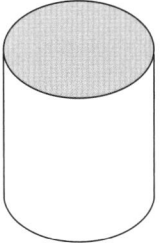

   (f)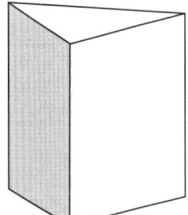

   _____   _____

2. Fill in the blanks.

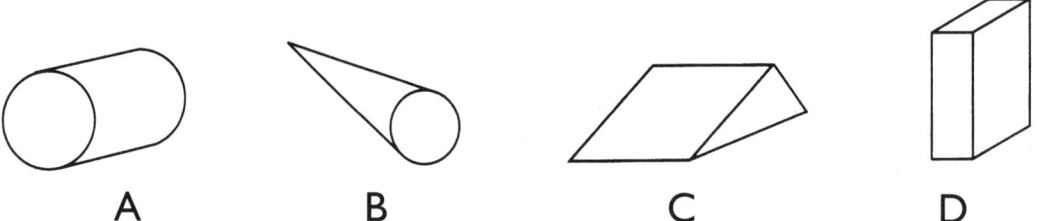

(a) Solid _____ has 5 flat faces.

(b) Solid _____ has 1 flat face and 1 curved face.

(c) Solid _____ has 2 flat faces and 1 curved face.

(d) Solid _____ has 6 flat faces.

(e) The 2 faces of Solid _____ are triangles.

3. Fill in the blanks.

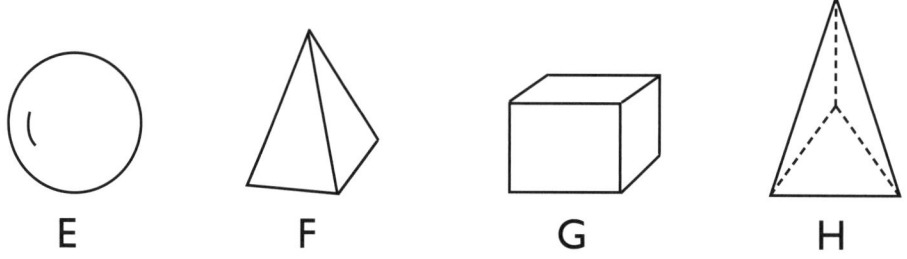

(a) Solid _____ has no vertices.

(b) Solid _____ has 5 vertices and 8 edges.

(c) Solid _____ has 8 vertices and 12 edges.

(d) Solid _____ has 6 flat faces.

(e) The 4 faces of Solid _____ are triangles.

Exercise 2 : Composite Figures

1. Join the two parts that form a square.

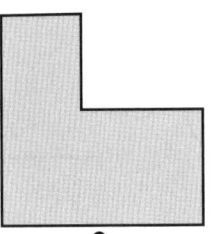 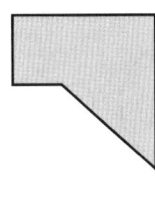 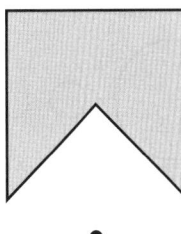 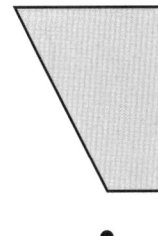

 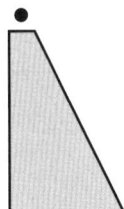  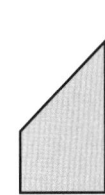

2. Draw a figure with two straight lines and two curves.

3. These are regular patterns of shapes.
   What shape comes next in each pattern?
   Fill in the blanks.

   (a) ◯ ∘ ∘ ◯ ∘ ∘ ◯ ∘ _____

   (b) △ ▭ △ ▭ _____

   (c) ⌒ ◗ ◖ ⌣ ⌒ ◗ _____

Exercise 3 : Angles and Shapes

1. Mark the angles of each figure.
   Then complete the table below.

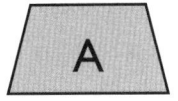
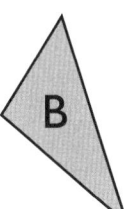

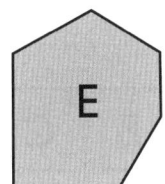
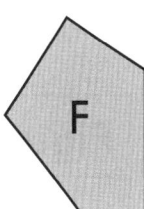

Polygon	Number of sides	Number of angles	Name of polygon
A			
B			
C			
D			
E			
F			

2. State how many angles each of the figures have.

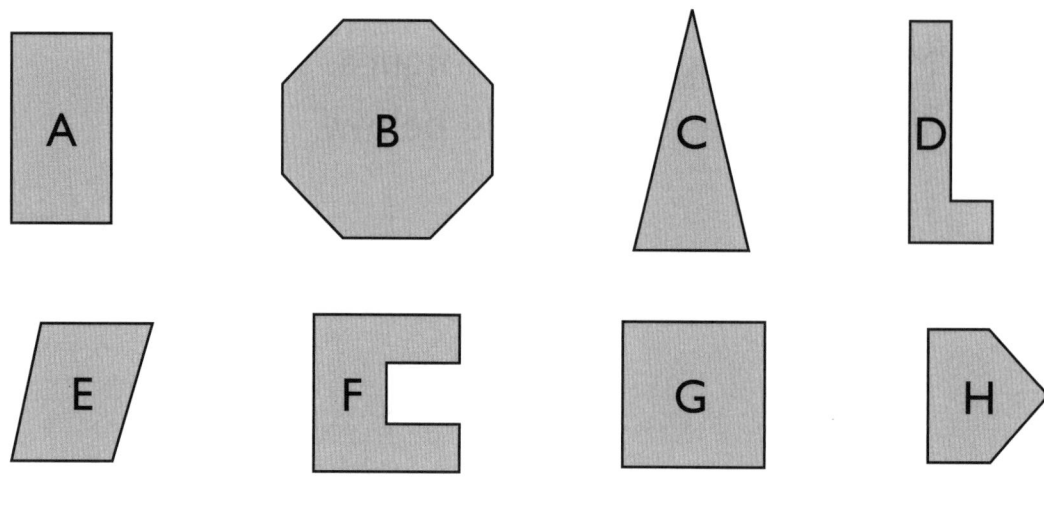

Figure	A	B	C	D	E	F	G	H	I
Number of angles									

3. Circle the polygons.

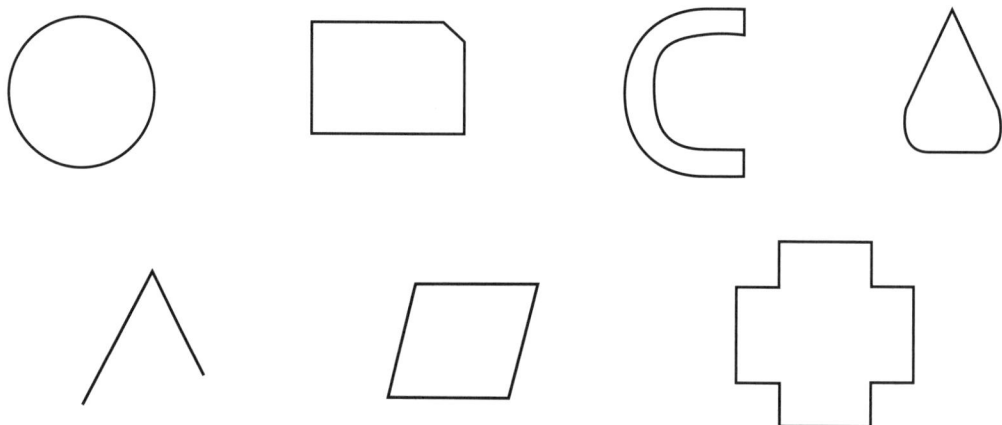

ANSWERS

Unit 1 Numbers to 1000
Exercise 1
1.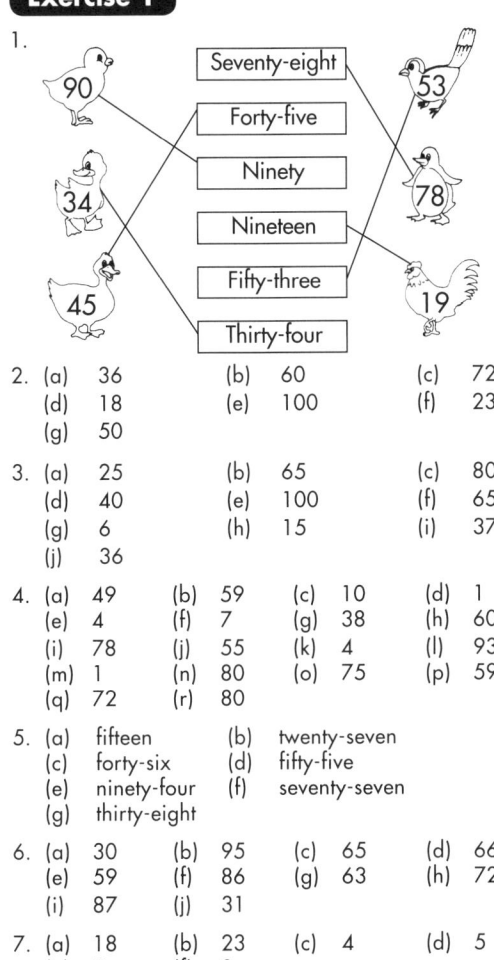

2. (a) 36   (b) 60   (c) 72
   (d) 18   (e) 100   (f) 23
   (g) 50
3. (a) 25   (b) 65   (c) 80
   (d) 40   (e) 100   (f) 65
   (g) 6   (h) 15   (i) 37
   (j) 36
4. (a) 49   (b) 59   (c) 10   (d) 1
   (e) 4   (f) 7   (g) 38   (h) 60
   (i) 78   (j) 55   (k) 4   (l) 93
   (m) 1   (n) 80   (o) 75   (p) 59
   (q) 72   (r) 80
5. (a) fifteen   (b) twenty-seven
   (c) forty-six   (d) fifty-five
   (e) ninety-four   (f) seventy-seven
   (g) thirty-eight
6. (a) 30   (b) 95   (c) 65   (d) 66
   (e) 59   (f) 86   (g) 63   (h) 72
   (i) 87   (j) 31
7. (a) 18   (b) 23   (c) 4   (d) 5
   (e) 9   (f) 0

Exercise 2
1.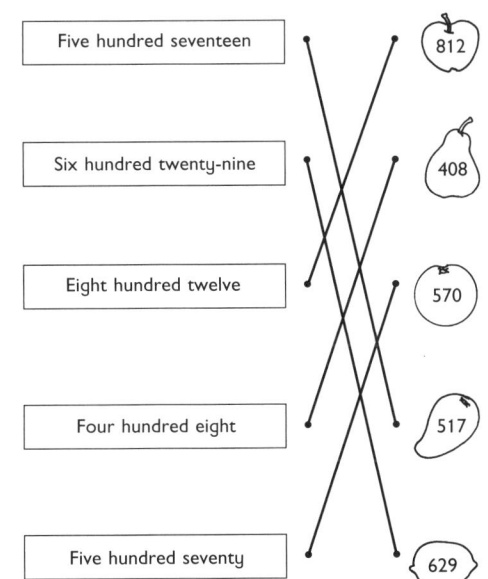

2. (a) 458   (b) 207   (c) 9   (d) 780
   (e) 4   (f) 7
3. (a) 834   (b) 509   (c) 680   (d) 372
4. (a) 899   (b) 503   (c) 603
   (d) 182 (e) 468   (f) 865
   (g) 10   (h) 10
5. (a) two hundred thirteen
   (b) three hundred fifty
   (c) five hundred fifteen
   (d) six hundred forty
   (e) eight hundred nine
   (f) four hundred forty-two
   (g) one hundred ninety-eight
   (h) three hundred seventy-five
   (i) seven hundred seventy-seven
   (j) nine hundred eighty-nine
6. (a) 1000 (b) 386   (c) 898   (d) 392
   (e) 700 (f) 960   (g) 70   (h) 110
7. (a) 136   (b) 805   (c) 770   (d) 345
   (e) 400 (f) 1   (g) 20   (h) 900

Exercise 3
1. (a) 54   (b) 170   (c) 198
2. (a) 66   (b) 445   (c) 281
3. (a) <   (b) >
4. (a) 36   (b) 262   (c) 366
   (d) 482 (e) 382   (f) 390
   (g) 423 (h) 548
5. (a) 225   (b) 156   (c) 169
   (d) 156 (e) 190   (f) 189
   (g) 228 (h) 569
6. (a) 268, 272, 359, 366
   (b) 579, 465, 281, 190
7. 143, 153, 183

Unit 2 Addition and Subtraction
Exercise 1A
1. (a) 22   (b) 15   (c) 4   (d) 8
   (e) 20   (f) 49   (g) 22   (h) 46
2. (a) 12   (b) 6   (c) 14   (d) 17
3. (a) 88   (b) 35
4. (a) 28 + 57 = 85; 57 + 28 = 85;
       85 − 28 = 57; 85 − 57 = 28
   (b) 59 + 37 = 96; 37 + 59 = 96;
       96 − 59 = 37; 96 − 37 = 59
   (c) 26 + 38 = 64; 38 + 26 = 64;
       64 − 38 = 26; 64 − 26 = 38

Exercise 1B
1. (a) 38   (b) 57 + 23 = 80, 80   (c) 13
   (d) 23   (e) 46

Exercise 2
1. (a) 8, 80, 800   (b) 9, 90, 900
   (c) 659   (d) 388   (e) 455   (f) 597
   (g) 667 (h) 539   (i) 678   (j) 798
   (k) 959
2. (a) 599   (b) 738   (c) 685

Exercise 3
1. (a) 3, 30, 300 (b) 5, 50, 500 (c) 843
   (d) 712 (e) 240 (f) 250
   (g) 332 (h) 106 (i) 6
   (j) 40 (k) 202
2. (a) 416 (b) 523 (c) 301
   (d) 76 (e) 710 (f) 25
   (g) 210 (h) 13
3. (a) 54 (b) 64 (c) 732
   (d) 512 (e) 602
4. (a) 242 (b) 323 (c) 606

Exercise 4A
1. (a) 10, 100, 800 (b) 12, 92, 892
   (c) 16, 160, 660 (d) 11, 41, 641
   (e) 13, 63, 463 (f) 15, 95, 695
2. (a) 62 (b) 92 (c) 174 (d) 570
   (e) 340 (f) 550 (g) 400 (h) 850
3. (a) 592 (b) 474 (c) 685 (d) 795
   (e) 667 (f) 849 (g) 900 (h) 957
4. (a) 738 (b) 825

Exercise 4B
1. (a) 732 (b) 443 (c) 783 (d) 815
   (e) 367 (f) 651 (g) 265 (h) 211
   (i) 182 (j) 749 (k) 588 (l) 799
   (m) 969 (n) 856 (o) 821 (p) 939
2. (a) 267 (b) 467 (c) 251

Exercise 5A
1. (a) 16 (b) 29 (c) 25 (d) 38
   (e) 26 (f) 18 (g) 6 (h) 7
   (i) 627 (j) 714 (k) 741 (l) 314
   (m) 107 (n) 258 (o) 662 (p) 90
2. (a) 183 (b) 61 (c) 118

Exercise 5B
1. (a) 278 (b) 419 (c) 528 (d) 848
   (e) 274 (f) 359 (g) 288 (h) 6
   (i) 125 (j) 302 (k) 754 (l) 877
   (m) 232 (n) 203 (o) 66 (p) 8
2. (a) 248 (b) 348 (c) 307

Unit 3 Length
Exercise 1
1. (a) 2 (b) 4 (c) 10 (d) 20
   (e) book, pencil or crayon
   (f) whiteboard
2. (a) 5 (b) 8 (c) 4 (d) C
   (e) A, C (f) B (g) A, B (h) B

Exercise 2
1. (a) No (b) Yes
2. (a) 68 (b) 93

Exercise 3
1. (a) 10 (b) 10 (c) 14 (d) 4 (e) 3
2. (a) 8 (b) 12 (c) B, A
3. Any 2 lines that are 4 cm and 7 cm long; C, D

Exercise 4
1. Answer varies
2. (a) No (b) Yes
3. more than
4. (a) 120 (b) 98
5. (a) 4 (b) 5 (c) 1 (d) 1
6. Answer varies for (a)-(d)
7. (a) 3 (b) 5 (c) 2
8. Yes

Unit 4 Multiplication and Division
Exercise 1
1. (a) 4+4+4=12, 12 (b) 3+3+3+3=12,12
   (c) 5+5+5+5 = 20, 20 (d) 18, 18
   (e) 18, 18 (f) 30, 30
   (g) 14, 14, 14 (h) 14, 14, 14
   (i) 24, 24 (j) 6 × 4 = 24, 24
   (k) 3 × 8 = 24, 24 (l) 3 × 6 = 18, 18
2. (a) 40, 40 (b) 18, 18
   (c) 10, 5, 10 (d) 21, 7, 21
3. (a) 8 × 4 = 32; 4 × 8 = 32
   (b) 6 × 5 = 30; 5 × 6 = 30
   (c) 5 × 8 = 40; 8 × 5 = 40
   (d) 2 × 10 = 20; 10 × 2 = 20

Exercise 2
1. (a) 5 (b) 6 (c) 4 (d) 6, 6
   (e) 4, 4 (f) 7, 7 (g) 6, 6
2. (a) 7, 4 (b) 8, 4 (c) 9, 2
3. (a) 30 ÷ 5 = 6; 30 ÷ 6 = 5
   (b) 27 ÷ 3 = 9; 27 ÷ 9 = 3
4. 4 × 6 = 24; 6 × 4 = 24;
   24 ÷ 4 = 6; 24 ÷ 6 = 4
5. (a) 24 ÷ 3 = 8, 8 (b) 24 ÷ 6 = 4, 4
   (c) 20 ÷ 5 = 4, 4 (d) 15 ÷ 5 = 3, 3
   (e) 12 ÷ 3 = 4, 4 (f) 20 ÷ 10 = 2, 2

Unit 5 Multiplication Tables of 2 and 3
Exercise 1
1.
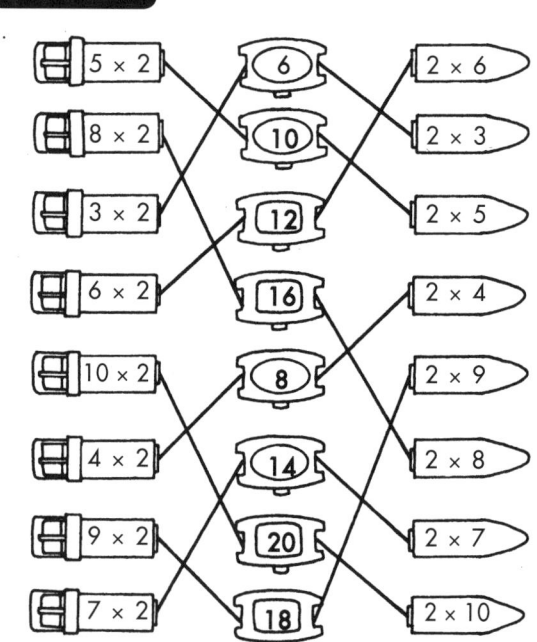

2.

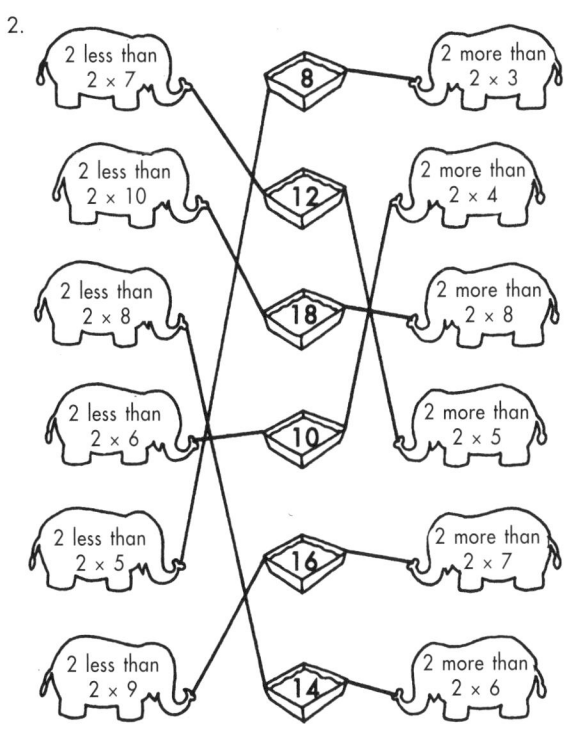

2.

3. (a) 20, 20 (b) 16, 16 (c) 18, 18
4. (a) ✔ (b) ✔ (c) ✗ (d) ✗
5. (a) $14 (b) 18 (c) 20

Exercise 2

1.

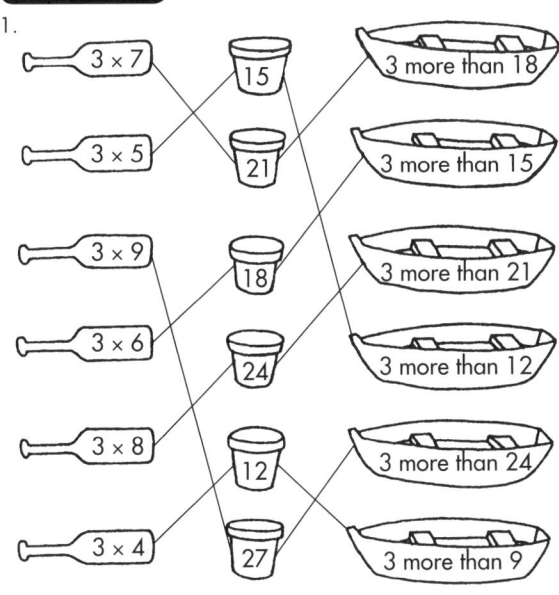

3. (a) 15, 15 (b) 24, 24 (c) 21, 21
   (d) 18, 18 (e) 27, 27

4. (a)

4	8	12	14	18	20	16
15	6	12	18	21	27	30	24

(b)

| 6 | 10 | 14 | 16 | 18 |

(c)

| 9 | 15 | 21 | 24 | 27 |

5. (a) ✔ (b) ✔ (c) ✔
6. (a) 15 (b) 21 (c) 30
   (d) 27 (e) 18 (f) 24

Exercise 3

1.

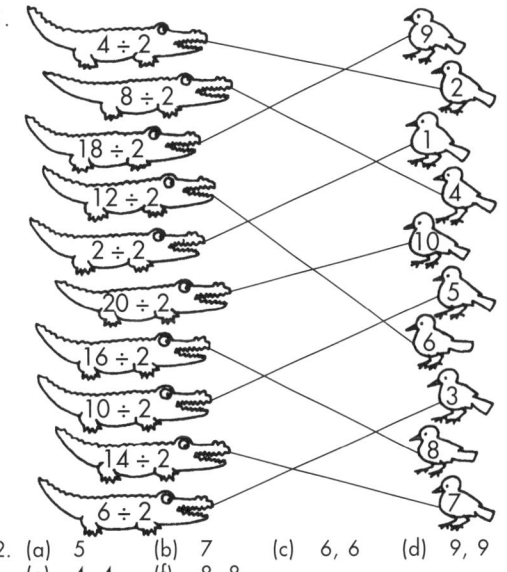

2. (a) 5 (b) 7 (c) 6, 6 (d) 9, 9
   (e) 4, 4 (f) 8, 8

3. (a) 4   (b) 8   (c) 6
   (d) 10 (e) 7   (f) 9

Exercise 4

1.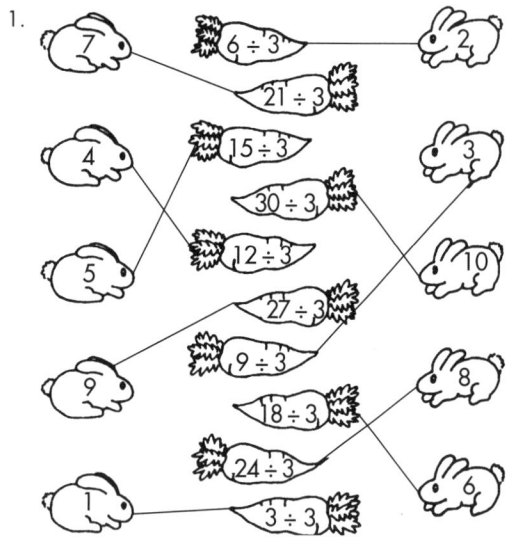

2. (a) 5   (b) 3   (c) 7   (d) 10
   (e) 8   (f) 6
3. (a) 8   (b) 9   (c) 7
   (d) 6   (e) 6   (f) 4

Exercise 5

1. 6, 2   (a) 6   (b) 2
2. (a) 1 (b) 4, 1

Unit 6 Addition and Subtraction

Exercise 1

1. (a) 76 (b) 26 (c) 45 (d) 60
2. (a) 50 (b) 80 (c) 95 (d) 90
   (e) 30 (f) 37 (g) 65
3. (a) 650 (b) 748 (c) 262 (d) 357
4. (a) 58 (b) 22 (c) 91
5. (a) 43 (b) 65 (c) 83 (d) 18

Exercise 2

1.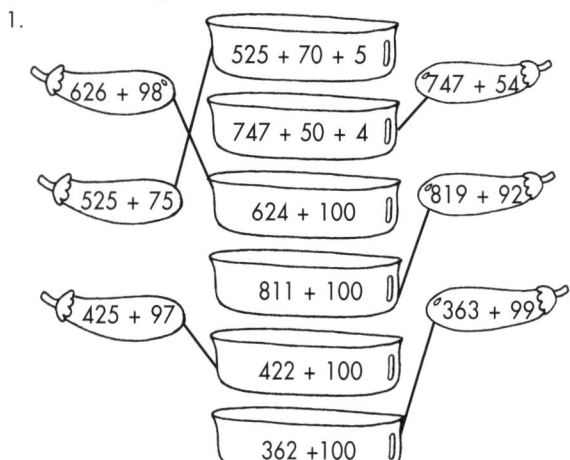

2. (a) 70 (b) 100 (c) 50 (d) 80 (e) 104 (f) 135
   (g) 386 (h) 260 (i) 605 (j) 794 (k) 931 (l) 780

Exercise 3

1.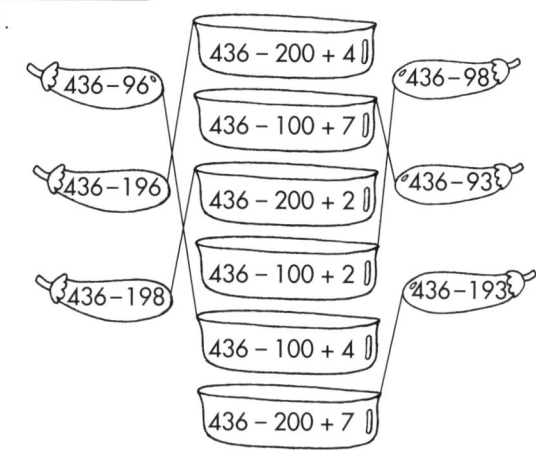

2. (a) 25 (b) 15 (c) 65 (d) 40
3. (a) 46 (b) 56 (c) 35 (d) 18
4. (a) 60, 360, 560   (b) 30, 330, 630
   (c) 85, 285, 485   (d) 35, 435, 735
5. (a) 24 (b) 33 (c) 19 (d) 35 (e) 521 (f) 310
   (g) 617 (h) 46 (i) 606 (j) 408 (k) 582 (l) 854

Unit 7 Multiplication and Division

Exercise 1

1. (a) 12, 12   (b) 20, 20
   (c) 24, 24   (d) 36, 36
2. (a) 12 (b) 24 (c) 36 (d) 32
3. (a) 16 (b) 24 (c) 28 (d) 36
4. (a) 6   (b) 5   (c) 9   (d) 10
5. (a) 3   (b) 8   (c) 7, 7
   (d) 9, 9 (e) 20, 20 (f) 40, 10
6. (a) $24 (b) 8 R 2 (c) 40
   (d) 7 days (e) 20 (f) 36

Exercise 2

1. (a) 25 (b) 40 (c) 35 (d) 50
2. (a) 20 (b) 15 (c) 2   (d) 8
   (e) 5   (f) 4
3. (a) 10, 2 (b) 35, 7 (c) 9, 9 (d) 6, 6
4. (a) 30 (b) 9 R 3 (c) $7

Exercise 3

1. (a) 40 (b) 60 (c) 80 (d) 100
   (e) 2   (f) 1   (g) 4   (h) 9
2. (a) 30, 3 (b) 70, 7
3. (a) $5 (b) $100 (c) $8 (d) 80

Unit 8 Money

Exercise 1

1. (a) 17.80 (b) 26.25 (c) 10.85
   (d) 28.05 (e) 70.50 (f) 21.55
2. (a) 0, 75 (b) 7, 35   (c) 12, 5
   (d) 48, 10 (e) 77, 15
3. (a) 0.95   (b) 6.05   (c) 18.60
   (d) 20.55 (e) 39.90

4. (a) 0.50 (b) 14.30
   (c) Fifteen dollars twenty-five cents
   (d) Forty dollars forty-five cents
   (e) $71.85
   (f) Ninety-eight dollars five cents
5. (a) 1.25 (b) 6.05 (c) 0.07
   (d) 0.60 (e) 2.35 (f) 5
6. (a) 95 (b) 165 (c) 283
   (d) 790 (e) 5 (f) 500
7. (a) 2.50 (b) 1 (c) 0.60
8. (a) 28 (b) 11 (c) 6
   (d) 19 (e) 100 (f) 60

Exercise 2
1. (a) 0.80 (b) 6 (c) 2.40 (d) 4
2. (a) 10.90 (b) 3.85 (c) 5.50 (d) 10.60
3. (a) 82 (b) 93 (c) 4.90 (d) 9.75
   (e) 8.80 (f) 7.24 (g) 9.65 (h) 17.10
4. (a) $2.24 (b) $4.01 (c) $3.47 (d) $8.00
   (e) $8.53 (f) $6.02
5. (a) $115 (b) $20 (c) $21.65 (d) $28.10

Exercise 3
1. (a) 0.95 (b) 0.99
2. (a) 6.25 (b) 0.15
3. (a) 13 (b) 12 (c) 4.20
   (d) 8.85 (e) 3.75 (f) 2.15
4. (a) $7.35 (b) $15.75 (c) $21.70

Unit 9 Fractions
Exercise 1
1. (a) No (b) Yes
2.
3.
4.

Exercise 2
1.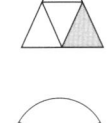

2. (a) $\frac{1}{4}$ (b) $\frac{3}{4}$ (c) $\frac{5}{8}$ (d) $\frac{7}{10}$
   (e) $\frac{3}{8}$ (f) $\frac{1}{3}$
3. (a) 1, 4, $\frac{1}{4}$ (b) 5, 9, $\frac{5}{9}$
   (c) 5, 8, $\frac{5}{8}$
4. (a) greater (b) smaller (c) smaller
   (d) greater (e) smaller
5. (a) $\frac{3}{4}$ (b) $\frac{4}{5}$
6. (a) $\frac{4}{5}$ (b) $\frac{3}{8}$
7. (a) $\frac{1}{3}$ (b) $\frac{1}{5}$
8. (a) $\frac{1}{8}$ (b) $\frac{1}{10}$
9. $\frac{1}{8}, \frac{1}{5}, \frac{1}{4}, \frac{1}{3}$
10. $\frac{1}{3}, \frac{1}{6}, \frac{1}{7}, \frac{1}{9}$
11. (a) $\frac{1}{3}$ (b) $\frac{5}{8}$
12. (a) $\frac{2}{3}$ (b) $\frac{1}{2}$

Unit 10 Time
Exercise 1
1. (a) 15 (b) 40 (c) 25
2. (a) 30 (b) 45 (c) 5 (d) 10
   (e) 15 (f) 40 (g) 20 (h) 50

Exercise 2
1. (a) 10, 5; 10, 5 (b) 15, 9; 15, 9
   (c) 25, 11; 25, 11 (d) 20, 1; 20, 1
2. (a) 5, 9 (b) 15, 2
   (c) 25, 8
3. (a) A.M. (b) P.M.
   (c) A.M. (d) P.M.

Unit 11 Tables and Graphs
Exercise 1
1. (a) 35 (b) 80
   (c) 24 (d) 21
   (e) △△△△△△△△△△
       (Accept other possible answers)
2. (a) 12 (b) 10
   (c) Football (d) 6
   (e) 6
3. (a) 24 (b) 28
   (c) 12 (d) 8
   (e) 40

4. (a) 6 (b) 12
   (c) 6 (d) 9
   (e) Penguin, Deer

Exercise 2

1. (a) 12 (b) 10 (c) 8 (d) 4 (e) 5
2. (a) 20 (b) 60 (c) 15 (d) 15

Exercise 3

1.

```
                        X
                        X
                        X
                        X
                        X       X
            X           X       X                X
            X           X       X                X
            X    X      X       X                X
            X    X      X       X                X
            X    X      X       X       X        X
            X    X      X       X       X        X
   X        X    X      X       X       X        X
   X        X    X      X       X       X        X
   X        X    X      X       X       X        X
   X        X    X      X       X       X        X
   X        X    X      X       X       X        X
  1A       1B   1C     1D      1E      1F       1G
                       Class
```

(a) 76 (b) 1D (c) 24
2. (a) 25 (b) 22 (c) Answers vary

Unit 12 Geometry

Exercise 1

1. (a) square (b) triangle (c) rectangle
   (d) circle (e) circle   (f) rectangle
2. (a) C (b) B (c) A (d) D (e) C
3. (a) E (b) F (c) G (d) G (e) H

Exercise 2

1.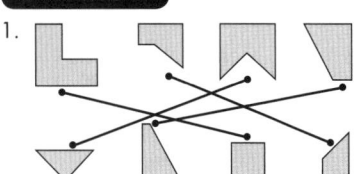

2. Accept any reasonable answers

3. (a) ○ (b) △ (c) ⌒

Exercise 3

1.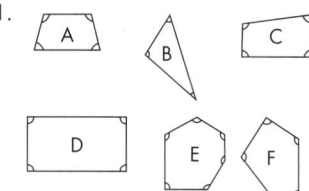

Polygon	Number of sides	Number of angles	Name of polygon
A	4	4	Quadrilateral
B	3	3	Triangle
C	4	4	Quadrilateral
D	4	4	Rectangle
E	6	6	Hexagon
F	5	5	Pentagon

2.

Figure	A	B	C	D	E	F	G	H
Number of angles	4	8	3	6	4	8	4	5

3.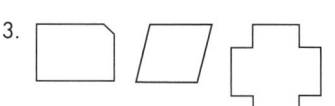